GROUP
INVOLVEMENT
TRAINING

A Step-by-Step Program
to Help Chronic Mentally
Ill Patients

CATHERINE HARTL CHAMBLISS, PH.D.

Copyright © 1988 by Catherine Hartl Chambliss
New Harbinger Publications, Inc.
5674 Shattuck Ave.
Oakland, CA 94609
Printed in the United States of America
All Rights Reserved
First printing July 1988, 3,000 copies

Table of Contents

Introduction

The plight of individuals suffering from chronic mental illness, especially schizophrenia, has been widely reported in professional literature and by the mass media. The unmet treatment needs of the two to three million people currently affected by schizophrenia are attracting increasing attention from the National Institute of Mental Health, Congress, and consumer groups.

Although current clinical literature cites the ability of psychotropic medications to control the "positive" symptoms of schizophrenia (hallucinations, delusions, disturbed psychomotor behavior, inappropriate affect), the "negative" symptoms (apathy, withdrawal, lack of interpersonal skills, perceived helplessness, and inability to use leisure time constructively) are largely unaffected by drug treatment. Increasingly, these are the types of disabling negative symptoms that are most problematic to patients and treatment staff alike.

In recent years, psychologists have played a major role in addressing the negative symptoms. Various psychosocial approaches have been shown to restore patient functioning and permit more successful deinstitutionalization. Of these methods, group therapy seems the most cost-effective approach. Although some structured group therapy guidelines are available (Goldstein et al., 1976; Wallace, 1982), they generally fail to address the particular psychosocial needs of many schizophrenic patients. These individuals need preliminary, positive experiences within therapeutic groups, without the demand to master specific, structured skills. This population is usually quite low functioning, hospitalized, and often suffers from chronic schizophrenia. A variety of factors such as medication side-effects, disorder symptoms, and the effects of institutionalization, make this group highly resistant to the very psychosocial interventions that are most needed to resume community living.

The available psychotherapeutic handbooks provide activities that are too advanced for many patients. Reaching these people requires inventive, individualized, creative, and appealing therapeutic tasks carefully designed to maximize success and to provide meaningful reinforcement. Flexible, structured patient activities are best because they allow opportunities for participants to make decisions and exert control. A decade of experimentation and clinical practice has enabled us to begin assembling a package of group techniques which helps patients progress to more advanced treatment and occupational training programs. We are eager to share our experiences with others.

In this book, the term "patient" is usually used to refer to the chronic mentally ill person because this program was developed in clinical settings in which this is the appropriate term. The author and publisher are well aware that many helping professionals in other settings will prefer the term "client."

Part I:
Group Involvement Training (GIT) Program

Program Overview and Rationale

As it enters its ninth year, our hospital Group Involvement Training (GIT) program is seen by patients and staff members as a valuable addition to the hospital's treatment program. The GIT three-tiered process was developed to meet the varied needs of the heterogeneous inpatient population. During the past eight years, the program has undergone substantial revision in order to keep up with current patient needs and changing staff interests, and to be compatible with staff and hospital schedules.

Presently forty patients regularly participate in at least one of the three program tiers. Transitions in program content are not uncommon. Our goal is to accommodate the interests of patients flexibly, in order to maximize motivation levels and encourage feelings of control. When participation levels are consistently high and members begin to see themselves as more competent and in control, the group setting becomes ideal for the development of social and adaptive living skills. Success in these groups makes its participants more eager to take advantage of more advanced therapeutic opportunities, often leading to eventual discharge.

Objectives and Principles

Common principles underlie all GIT groups.

Generally, these groups are designed to provide patients with learning experiences intended to increase **participation in therapeutic activities,** enhance perceived **self-efficacy,** and improve **social skills.** Greater involvement is promoted by providing a variety of engaging tasks in a supportive and personalized atmosphere. Improving perceived self-efficacy and hardiness is achieved by offering diverse opportunities for mastery, growth, and personal control. Social skills are fostered through practice within a setting where responsive feedback can encourage appropriate, successful approaches to others.

Therapeutic Participation Goal

One of the primary treatment obstacles in psychiatric hospital environments is patient refusal to participate in therapeutic programs. Mandatory treatment activities only partially circumvent this problem, because all too often patients meet the letter, but disregard the "spirit" of the "law." (Patients' perfunctory, passive attendance should not be confused with active, productive involvement.) Since motivating patients to be open to learning experiences is of such major concern, the GIT program has been designed to maximize patient involvement. Appealing tasks and enthusiastic, supportive leaders make patients willing to operate within a structured group program. Graduates of the preliminary GIT groups take with them to other therapeutic group settings and to work environments a positive feeling about group involvement.

The groups are guided by leaders, who select tasks that assure a high probability of success. (When very difficult tasks are attempted, patients are carefully shown how to break them down into simpler components.) Effective completion of a variety of interesting tasks is self-reinforcing and socially reinforced. In addition, leaders encourage and applaud effort, even when success is not achieved. Jointly, this has increased members' motivation level and willingness to take learning risks, thus paving the way for further growth in both a general and a group-specified way.

GIT groups usually meet twice a week. This frequency assures continuity for patients who may have learning impairments that limit memory. Meetings involve group tasks which are isolated events taking no more than one meeting, or tasks that are part of longer term projects requiring more sessions. A consistent meeting time, ideally integrated into the rest of the patients' schedule, for example, right after lunch or afternoon medications, helps to maximize punctuality. By supportively encouraging a patient to give the group a try (even if at first the person just chooses to watch and listen from a distance), we have found that in one to three months' time, most individuals in GIT have learned to operate comfortably and reliably within a structured group setting, and to recognize and anticipate the rewards of attendance.

Simple, inexpensive refreshments (decaffeinated coffee or iced tea, powdered soft drinks, etc.) can be prepared and served by the patients. By making such drinks contingent on participation, the group leader reinforces responsible involvement. We have found it best to limit the scope of refreshments; elaborate feasts create high expectations that can become burdensome to meet. It's also important to avoid making food consumption a major group focus. However, this does not mean that occasional treats should be avoided; group planning for special occasions often includes special, attractive foods.

Participation in the group also demonstrates how patients can develop their own recreational and social opportunities, and make use of available hospital entertainment and learning resources. Members are encouraged to take advantage of all hospital therapeutic opportunities.

Occasionally, activities that originate in the meetings extend into the nongroup social lives of members, for example, after a group meeting that involved teaching card games, for a time card-playing was continued throughout the week. This form of recreation served as a mechanism for patient improvement of conditions and relationships within the building.

Self-Efficacy Goal

One central objective of the program involves altering patients' expectations about the relationship between actions and reward. Many inpatients show depressed motivation levels to change and learning because of an erroneous belief that their behavior "makes no difference." Passivity and negativeness are understandable in light of preconceived ideas of powerlessness. Such individuals can benefit from activities that help them recognize how instrumental they are in shaping their lives and improving their circumstances. This recognized instrumentality, or perceived self-efficacy, is fostered through various means within the program.

In developing group activities, efforts are made to provide experiences that counter the "learned helplessness" commonly exhibited by inpatients who believe that events of their lives are totally controlled by outside forces. GIT emphasizes the importance of patient input and suggestions for group activities. Members are encouraged to assume some group responsibilities, which in turn demonstrates to the participants their potential to influence outcomes.

In order to reduce learned helplessness effects it is necessary to program for mastery by teaching in a manner that emphasizes and clarifies response-reinforcer conditions. The ultimate goal of mastery over significant life events may start with mundane accomplishments, such as learning to polish one's own shoes or prepare refreshments. Accomplishing such a task teaches a person more than shoe polishing or coffee-making, it teaches that "I can do something!" Not only is the patient reinforced, but the staff may be encouraged to reevaluate their pervasive negative conceptions about the learning abilities and potential of inpatients. To reduce certain learned deficits, patients must be taught about choices and how to make them. The ability of a patient to carry out a personal choice is a cornerstone of independent functioning. Individuals must be *allowed* the opportunity to make choices in a variety of areas, for example, types of programming activities, order of task presented, and participation in programming. The range of programmatic services can and ought to be personalized—patients should be allowed to make their own choices.

The groups are structured to encourage patient initiative and allow as much patient control as possible. Participants make key contributions in planning and preparing for meetings. This sense of *ownership* makes successful undertakings doubly rewarding. Patient control provides members with a sense of group pride and reduces the generalized expectancy of helplessness. In turn, greater motivation to learn and try new things is developed. Furthermore, group planning and choosing provide practice with important organization and problem-solving skills.

Techniques designed to encourage patients' realistic sense of personal control, to increase a sense of commitment to their life's goals, and to create helpful attitudes toward change improve members' capacity to deal with stressful situations. Group members are encouraged to perceive life changes as challenging opportunities for growth, rather than as threats to their security. Modifying patients' interpreta-

tions of ongoing changes in their lives, for example, discharge, facility transfer, staff relocation, etc., assists individuals in responding to these events more flexibly, optimistically, and constructively. Since many of the patients have consistently avoided making positive life changes and postponed opportunities for growth because of their fear of failure and an unwillingness to take risks, modifying their conception of change may lead to their achieving a variety of treatment objectives. Increasing patients' resistance to stress will both improve their coping while in the hospital and permit them to make more successful, long-term adjustments upon community reentry.

By valuing the patient's instrumentality and providing opportunities for its development, the program heightens the beliefs of the patients that they can constructively shape their own futures.

Social Skills Goal

Social skills can atrophy when disused. Another major objective of the program is to contribute to the quality of patients' social lives. Although many hospital functions encourage social interaction, these therapeutic groups serve as useful additional mechanisms for interpersonal growth. The groups promote positive social participation and foster and support patients engaged in the difficult task of building friendly relationships. The requisite social skills for optimal interpersonal functioning in most hospital or clinical settings are numerous. Many hospital residents and patients can be challenging to interact with, even for those individuals with substantial coping skills. For patients whose frustration tolerance and comprehension have been compromised by mental illness, the task of developing and maintaining mutually supportive relationships is quite difficult.

GIT members learn and rehearse the names of other patients. Serving as task partners provides shared experiences, which form the basis for later conversations. Volunteer group assistants, who are expected to prepare and serve refreshments, hand out supplies, or take attendance, are respected by the others and develop special familiarity with GIT leaders. Revolving these responsibilities gives all members the chance to serve the group's needs, fosters cooperation among patients, and develops more flexible attitudes toward social roles and responsibilities. GIT members develop communication skills through planning, decision-making, and role-playing activities. Varied joint projects help to build sensitivity to others' needs and encourages an appreciation of individual strengths and weaknesses. Teaching and community projects remind patients of the problems of others, and allow members to take pleasure in nurturing and helping those less fortunate. GIT members gain a great deal of experience in supporting one another: learning to give and receive compliments and to feel pride in the group. The simple existence of a network of resocialization groups challenges the erroneous belief that patients can't befriend and provide assistance for one another.

The presence of staff members, who are sometimes assisted by volunteer paraprofessionals, gives the group the opportunity to learn through observation. The patients generally perceive the volunteers as competent and attractive (powerful), helpful and caring (nurturant), and open and disclosing (enhancing perceived similarity), which helps to maximize the volunteers' effectiveness as role models. Patient communication skills are also enhanced by observing these models.

The presence of several sensitive staff members who show genuine respect for the patients is intended to facilitate smoother social interrelationships among hospital patients during nongroup hours. With the aid of staff "arbitrators," members have worked to resolve certain differences and have experienced the enjoyment of more open communication. This seems to have left many with a greater

appreciation of their fellow hospital residents, which in turn produces more positive social feedback to enhance feelings of self-worth. By increasing self-worth and acceptance, defensiveness and interpersonal conflict are reduced. Watching interesting, enthusiastic and personable volunteers enjoy relationships with patients has led some individuals to take a second, less critical and more trusting look at their fellow patients. As a result, some have taken a less critical look at themselves as well.

The establishment of an in-building support network and the continued development of positive relationships among patients is an important objective of the program. The expectation is that those patients who are successful in developing workable and satisfying social strategies within the hospital will be much better equipped for eventual community placement.

GIT Effectiveness: Program Evaluation

After the GIT Program had been in its development stage for three years, a program evaluation was performed. This experimental clinical study was conducted in order to assess the efficacy of the GIT approach.

Method

Forty-eight inpatients with primary diagnoses of schizophrenia of the chronic undifferentiated type were randomly assigned by sex to either the GIT treatment group (11 females, 13 males) or the waiting-list control (12 females, 12 males) group. All participants resided in the same unlocked, coed psychiatric unit at Norristown State Hospital in Pennsylvania.

GIT Treatment Group (GTG): All GIT treatment participants were invited to attend regularly scheduled one hour group meetings, twice weekly, for twelve weeks. Two groups of twelve patient members were created. All group meetings were conducted by the same three coleaders (undergraduate psychology majors with at least one year's experience as a GIT group coleader). On-site supervision was provided by a licensed clinical psychologist. At the end of each meeting, coleaders reviewed the session, analyzed their success in implementing GIT objectives, and planned ways to foster these objectives in the next planned group activity. Group sessions took place at a large table in a spacious day hall. Patient members were encouraged to attend meetings without prompting. When some members failed to arrive on time, they were approached by a volunteer, who reminded them of the meeting.

Pretest measures were administered during the first three weeks of group sessions. Pairs of raters observed patients during these six meetings, and completed six behavioral measures for each patient during a meeting. In order to familiarize the patients with the raters, during the two weeks prior to commencing treatment, the raters spent a few hours every week in the day hall at group meetings, casually socializing with the patients. During the six pretest sessions, raters observed members as unobtrusively as possible by sitting a few feet outside of the large group circle. Ratings for attendance and punctuality were completed after the first five minutes of each session. After the close of a meeting, summary ratings for group involvement, initiation, verbal communication, and helping behavior were made. For each six behavioral measures, mean ratings for the six pretest sessions were totalled for each participant. This same ratings' procedure was followed during the posttest period. Three self-report questionnaires were completed by patient members during the second, fourth, and fifth meetings. The supervising psychologist obtained ratings of patients' involvement in outside ac-

tivities by reviewing individual charts and progress notes just prior to the first scheduled group meeting.

Behavioral posttest ratings were obtained during the last six sessions. The three self-report instruments were readministered during the twentieth, twenty-second, and twenty-third group sessions. Posttreatment outside involvement was assessed via chart reviews conducted two weeks after the last scheduled meeting. (This allowed time for relevant notes to be written by support staff.)

Waiting List Control (WLC): Participants in the waiting list control group were *not* assigned to a GIT group during the twelve-week experimental period, but were invited to join a GIT group within two months following the study. These patients were asked to complete the three self-report scales on the same days that GIT members were taking these tests. WLC and GTG participants' charts and progress notes were reviewed concurrently, in order to evaluate their outside activities involvement. No behavioral ratings of WLC participants were made.

Dependent Variables

In order to measure patient response to GIT groups, three basic variables reflecting the therapeutic objectives of the group involvement training program were considered: level of participation, self-efficacy, and socialization.

Participation level was assessed through measuring scales for group attendance and punctuality, and for patient involvement in therapeutic activities within and outside of group meetings. Self-efficacy was measured behaviorally by rating patients' initiating actions within group sessions. In addition, patients were asked to complete two self-report scales, the Nowicki-Strickland Locus of Control Scale (1973) and the Inpatient Locus of Control Scale (1980), a situationally-tied locus of control scale based on specific hospital experiences. Each of these two scales yielded scores indicating the patient's degree of internality versus externality. Socialization was assessed through two behavioral ratings: verbal communication (receptive and expressive behavior) and helping behavior displayed during group sessions. A self-report scale measured attitudes toward other patients.

In completing all self-report scales, participants who had reading difficulties were provided with an individual helper to read and clarify items. Since several GTG and WLC patients at first refused to complete the self-report scales, it was often necessary to approach them a second time, after a brief delay, to get them to finish. Behavioral raters were pretrained in the use of all rating measures and were given prior practice administering these scales to inpatients during sample group sessions. Interrater reliabilities for the seven rating scales were all high.

Results

Pretreatment equivalence of the GTG and WLC groups was assessed by comparing pretest scores on locus of control, patient attitude, and outside involvement. No significant differences on any of these measures were found. (See the samples of rating measures used in the study and tables of the results following this discussion.)

Comparison of GTG and WLC group posttest scores revealed significant differences on all four measures. The GTG participants scored in a more internal direction on both indicators of locus of control than did WLC participants. GTG members also scored impressively higher on the patient attitudes scale. On the posttest measure of outside therapeutic and work activities involvement, GTG members showed greater improvement than did the WLC participants, although members of both groups did show gains. On the patient attitude posttest measure, the GTG scores were significantly higher than those of the WLC group.

Pretreatment-Posttreatment Comparisons

The GIT treatment group showed marked improvement on all three behavioral group participation measures. Comparison of pretest and posttest scores points to significant increases in attendance, punctuality, and group involvement. The increase in outside activity involvements was also impressive.

The GTG failed to show significant change on the two locus of control measures, possibly because of group variability. The behavioral initiation measure revealed gains in the pretreatment-posttreatment comparisons.

The behavioral scales measuring social behavior within the group showed meaningful gains in verbal communication and helping behavior. On the self-report indicator of attitudes toward other patients, the GTG also increased significantly.

Comparisons of the GTG and WLC groups suggest that GIT participation fosters development of a more internal locus of control orientation and encourages more positive attitudes among patients. GIT participation also was associated with greater increases in outside therapeutic and work activity involvements. Although both groups demonstrated increased participation in outside activities, the posttest scores of the GTG members were more than double those of the WLC group. (The score increase was anticipated given the hospital's push for more therapeutic participation. In part, it also may have been due to an unexpected step-up in hospital offerings of occupational and recreational therapies at this particular time.) These involvement findings are consistent with both the locus of control and patient attitude changes observed in the GIT treatment group. A more internal direction is associated with greater coping behavior—perceiving outcomes as a result of one's own efforts may increase motivation to participate in therapeutic activities. More positive attitudes toward fellow patients may also encourage greater outside involvement, since most activities require peer interactions.

Review of the pretreatment-posttreatment score comparisons suggests that the GIT groups significantly affected patients' behavior both within and outside group sessions. At the conclusion of the treatment module, GIT members were much more involved in the group process than they had been at the outset. Their attendance, punctuality, and group participation all increased. Clearly, the GIT approach succeeded in motivating greater group involvement. Since GIT's aim is to provide "stepping-stone" experiences to foster patients' interest in available therapeutic and occupational resources, it is important to consider the GIT training group outside involvement findings. At the end of the twelve-week treatment module, GIT members were attending more occupational and recreational ther-

apy activities, participating in the on-grounds sheltered workshops to a greater extent, and expressing more positive attitudes about individual therapy, technical and business school involvement, and eventual discharge.

The indicators of self-efficacy provided a contradictory picture in the pretest-posttest comparisons. Scores measuring patients' initiating behavior within the group revealed meaningful gains, suggesting that the GIT approach was successful in fostering patient confidence, assertiveness, and risk-taking. However, the changes in locus of control were not statistically noteworthy. The relative stability of scores on these measures may have contributed to a failure to observe changes over the course of the twelve-week treatment period. A more extended GIT treatment experience

---

Comparison of GIT Treatment and Waiting List Control Groups

	GIT	Waiting List Control
No. of Participants:	24	24

Pretest: No significant differences found on:
- Locus of Control measures
- Peer Rating Scale
- Outside Involvement Rating

Posttest:

Nowicki-Strickland Locus of Control*
	GIT	Waiting List Control
	x̄ 43.5	x̄ 48.5
	sd 9.57	sd 6.6

Inpatient Locus of Control**
	GIT	Waiting List Control
	x̄ 32.92	x̄ 39.25
	sd 8.65	sd 4.67

Peer Rating Scale**
	GIT	Waiting List Control
	x̄ 16.21	x̄ 12.96
	sd 3.16	sd 2.88

Outside Involvement Rating***
	GIT	Waiting List Control
	x̄ 38.67	x̄ 18.08
	sd 11.73	sd 10.93

* $p < .05$
** $p < .01$
*** $p < .001$

might show the expected increases in internal locus of control. In addition, inspection of locus of control score changes indicated substantial variability among group members. While many participants displayed the expected increase in internality, several actually scored in the more external direction after treatment. Perhaps features of the group experience interacted with personality characteristics to produce these differential effects. Future investigations might attempt to describe this possible interaction.

GIT participation was associated with improvement on the three socialization measures. At the end of the treatment module, group members talked, listened, and helped one another more than they had at the beginning. They also expressed more favorable attitudes toward their group peers. Future research might assess whether these more positive feelings extended beyond the group to other hospital patients, or whether these attitudes were confined to just the individuals who had shared GIT experiences.

Pretreatment-Posttreatment Comparisons

	Pretreatment X (s.d.)	Posttreatment X (s.d.)
Attendance	5.13 (2.51)	10.04 (2.31) ***
Punctuality	6.13 (2.52)	10.92 (1.84) ***
Group Involvement	8.71 (5.47)	21.67 (5.92) ***
Outside Involvement	15.92 (12.29)	38.67 (11.73) ***
Nowicki/Strict. LOC	41.25 (8.84)	43.50 (9.57) ns
Inpatient LOC	33.79 (8.29)	32.92 (8.65) ns
Behavior Initiation	3.50 (1.89)	7.79 (3.64) ***
Verbal Communication	6.46 (5.93)	15.42 (6.17) **
Helping Behavior	2.83 (1.37)	6.00 (3.19) **
Peer Rating Scale	14.92 (3.48)	16.21 (3.16) *

* $p < .05$
** $p < .01$
*** $p < .001$

GIT Behavioral Rating Scales

Member's Name: _____   **Date:** _____

Participation

Attendance: 0 . . . . 1 2
                      absent   needed   on time
                                   reminder

Punctuality: 0 . . . . 1 2
                   >= 5 minutes   <5 minutes   on time
                      early   late

Involvement:

0 . . . . 1 . . . . 2 . . . . 3 . . . . 4 5

| left early | sat unresponsively passive | pursues irrelevant task; resists instructions | actively follows directions until frustrated | actively follows directions; succeeds at task | actively follows directions; completes task; leads when asked |

Self-Efficacy

Initiation: 0 . . . . 1 2
                      none   requires   spontaneous
                                  prompting   self-expression

Social Skills

Communication:

0 . . . . 1 . . . . 2 . . . . 3 4

| isolated | listens silently | answers others | some spontaneous speech | high spontaneous speech; seeks listeners |

Helping: 0 . . . . 1 2
                      none   only when   spontaneous
                                   asked   helping;
                                                volunteers

Peer Rating Scale

	not at all or never (0)	sometimes (1)	always (2)
1. I think the other people in this group are nice and friendly.	0	1	2
2. I think the other people in this group are selfish.	0	1	2
3. I think the other people in this group are stupid.	0	1	2
4. I think the other people in this group have good ideas.	0	1	2
5. I think the other people in this group are too loud.	0	1	2
6. It's fun to talk to people in the group.	0	1	2
7. It's nice to see the people in the group.	0	1	2
8. I like to be with the other people in this group.	0	1	2
9. It's nice to live with the people on this floor.	0	1	2
10. The other people in this group are friends of mine.	0	1	2

Inpatient Locus of Control Scale (Templin & Chambliss, 1980)

1. Do you feel there is little you can do to improve your performance on games you play?

2. Do you have a lot of choice about who your friends are on the ward?

3. Do you feel that some patients get special treatment from staff members for no reason?

4. Do you feel that working hard will help you get money?

5. Do you feel that problems you have with medication will eventually get better on their own?

6. Do you feel that planning ahead will help you budget your limited number of cigarettes?

7. Do you feel only lucky people get as much coffee as they want?

8. Do you feel that you have to try hard to get better?

9. Do you feel that wishing will help you get to live in the building you desire?

10. Do you feel that you have a lot of choice in deciding what activities you do?

11. Do you feel that it doesn't pay to try hard to stop smoking because there is nothing you can do to stop?

12. Do you feel that planning ahead will help you find more interesting things to do with your free time?

13. Do you often find that wishing someone was your friend will make him or her your friend?

14. Do you feel that you can do a lot to get help for problems you have?

15. Do you feel that problems you have with people will just work themselves out?

16. Do you have to try hard to be friends with certain people who you want to be friends with?

Scored Answers to Inpatient Locus of Control Scale

1.	yes	9.	yes
2.	no	10.	no
3.	yes	11.	yes
4.	no	12.	no
5.	yes	13.	yes
6.	no	14.	no
7.	yes	15.	yes
8.	no	16.	no

The GIT Manual

There is a clear need for this resource of concrete information about specific activities designed to reduce the symptoms of this highly disabled, chronic population. Staff members mandated to develop psychosocial rehabilitation programs are stymied by the lack of a convenient, well-organized resource book. Up until now, psychologists, psychiatric nurses, aides, counselors, and therapists have had to develop their own structured interventions from scratch, often operating in a vacuum. This obviously has been inefficient.

Mental health institutions need this manual to streamline their treatment planning process. It facilitates the process by giving specific detailed descriptions of varied group activities already proven to be helpful in addressing the needs of the chronic schizophrenic population. This guide's organization permits more individualized treatment planning, because it relates each activity to specific patient needs and group activities by patient function-

ing levels. The step-by-step guidelines for organizing, preparing, and implementing each activity are supplemented by instructions for modifying activities to meet specific patient needs.

This book has been structured to ease some of the documentation burden of mental health facilities by providing a clear, concise therapeutic rationale for each activity. Staff members using this resource will have more time to invest in hands-on patient contact. This guide will also allow relatively inexperienced helpers to interact with patients in goal-directed, effective ways. We have had extensive and successful experience with paraprofessionals using the techniques noted in this manual.

Our years of experience with over a thousand patients and staff members have made us well aware of the frustrations inherent in treating chronic illness. We have included many supportive suggestions aimed at helping group leaders maintain their enthusiasm and optimism. The upbeat, encouraging tone may prove to be one of this book's most valuable assets.

Part II: GIT Program Administration

Staffing

Addressing the Needs of Caregivers and Patients

Many chronically mentally ill patients challenge the facilities and people that serve their needs. Often pathology, medication side-effects, and a history of hospitalization combine to produce apathy and resistance in these patients. Reluctance to participate in therapeutic programs frustrates staff members and contributes to a high rate of "burnout" among these mental health workers. Caregivers frequently respond by retreating from all but mandated contact with patients, rarely working to develop new mutual activities. The burned out staff creates norms which are difficult for enthusiastic newcomers to violate. Those who care deeply and want to foster greater patient involvement by developing appropriate, relatively undemanding patient tasks find that their ideas are granted little respect. The "low level" and simple social activities caring staff propose are sometimes difficult to classify as formal therapy, and are too easily dismissed as unimportant or unproductive.

In our experience at the state hospital, it has become clear that it is precisely these low level and simple activities that can often best pave the way for future formal therapeutic involvement among the chronically mentally ill. These activities can enhance patient self-esteem, diminish social anxiety, and produce vital motivation to change. The GIT approach formally recognizes many chronic pa-

tients' needs for preparatory therapeutic training. Rather than allowing this important element of the treatment process to be ignored or dismissed, we need to understand these helpful techniques more fully and expand their implementation.

There are many caregivers who want to play a greater role in the helping process but don't know where to start. This manual provides concrete, step-by-step instructions on how to develop a GIT group. The methods we describe don't assume prior clinical experience or a professional educational background. Indeed, for over a decade we have been encouraging community volunteers to implement these techniques at our institution, and have witnessed their success.

The GIT approach to reach the chronic psychiatric patient also legitimizes many of the staff members' ideas for activities. It makes it easier for these caregivers to implement different patient activities without fearing their efforts will be dismissed as unimportant. Furthermore, the GIT approach helps the caregivers to better articulate the underlying psychological objectives of efforts to enhance patient involvement. Documenting these objectives into the treatment plan is then made easier. This can increase the visibility of their helping efforts, provide recognition to the committed, enthusiastic staff members, and satisfy the institution's need to document the reasons for including certain methods in the plan. We have also provided caregivers with appropriate tools to help them evaluate and describe the progress of the chronic patient.

We have designed the GIT program with the needs of both patients and caregivers in mind. A set of therapeutic activities can only help patients if the caregiver remains committed and enthusiastic. Since the schizophrenic population typically experiences gradual progress, marked by occasional relapses, GIT group leaders can't rely solely on patient improvement to sustain motivation. For this reason we have worked to make the activities inherently reinforcing or relaxing for *all* group members. We emphasize the need to recognize the value of achieving subgoals. The time-limited modular GIT structure provides all participants with a periodic sense of task completion and success.

GIT Leaders

Multiple Leadership: It is advantageous to have more than one leader for each GIT group that is developed. Multiple leadership is an obvious asset during the early stages of group formation, when resistant prospective members often need considerable individual coaxing. While one leader can attend to the needs of the group members already in attendance, the remaining leader(s) can attempt to draw out recalcitrant people who want special attention before they are willing to cooperate. The individual differences among leaders elicit varying responses from patients. Having multiple leaders increases the likelihood that patients will find someone they feel they can "click" with, facilitating the rapport necessary for any therapeutic relationship.

After the GIT group membership has stabilized, having more than one leader helps to sustain the group's energy level. Multiple leadership provides staff with a built-in source of mutual support. Rotating group responsibilities among leaders can reduce the possibility of staff burnout. We have found that with this type of activity-focused group experience it is not absolutely necessary to have the same leaders present at every meeting. (With more traditional group therapies, a set group of leaders is recommended.)

The multiple leadership system can be used in GIT because meetings tend to be quite present-centered, with an emphasis on here-and-now interactions among patients. Although ongoing relationships certainly develop among members, the main thrust of the group process is not an in-depth exploration of these relationships. Occasional leader absences seem to be tolerated quite well by GIT participants, as long as there is minimal disruption of the basic meeting schedule. These patients are often challenged by the demand to remember group meeting times and must work hard to report for sessions without prompting. It can be quite frustrating for members to remember to come to a meeting only to discover that it was unexpectedly cancelled. A corps of alternate group leaders with some familiarity with the participants and GIT group framework can substantially reduce the risk of such countertherapeutic experiences. In emergencies, we have found that the more experienced patient members can be designated group assistant leaders to guide the group in a simple task when a staff leader is unavailable for a meeting. These situations, although rare, clearly convey group ownership to patients.

Multidisciplinary Staffing: There are several advantages to involving staff from various treatment disciplines in the GIT program. Leaders with different training backgrounds contribute to a well-rounded group. Staff members from different departments (for example, occupational, recreational, music, and horticultural therapies and social work, psychology, and psychiatry) have access to various resources and equipment which can enrich the group experience. Varied interests among leaders keep the groups stimulating for patient members and illustrates the benefits of differences among people.

Patient Coleaders: In order to emphasize patient ownership and control of the GIT group process, it's advantageous to make patient members responsible for basic tasks central to group maintenance whenever feasible. Appointing "group assistants" to perform routine tasks confers a certain amount of prestige on them, and provides them with opportunities to become more highly identified with the GIT leaders. Experienced group assistants are viewed as authorities in their domain, possessing the power to make small decisions that affect other members in the group experience. Leaders supervise these assistants and help them make and convey appropriate decisions to the others. We have found that group assistants take immense pride in their jobs and usually welcome the opportunity to have greater control over their environment. Learning how to handle responsibilities, make decisions, and communicate choices to others can obviously profit the patient assistant.

GIT patient assistants can be given responsibility for the following kinds of tasks:

- arranging chairs prior to meetings
- carrying supplies to group table
- distributing task supplies
- preparing task materials in advance
- taking attendance
- preparing simple refeshments
- handing out refreshments
- cleaning tables after meetings
- distributing invitations to new members
- preparing announcement posters
- operating tape recorder with music tasks
- collecting ballots during voting tasks
- arranging completing art projects
- organizing communal storage cabinet

Paraprofessionals: In developing GIT groups for individuals at Norristown, it soon became obvious that the patients' needs rapidly outstripped the staff energy available to meet them. In order to satisfy the diverse and pressing demands of our patients, we decided to make a specially trained corps of undergraduate student volunteers an integral part of the group program.

Undergraduate psychology majors are usually bewildered by the wide variety of postgraduate options available to those with an expressed commitment to helping people. This confusion is often associated with some ambivalence about choosing a clinical career that will require close contact with "deviant" members of the population. (Fear of prospective patients is fairly common among clinically oriented undergraduates.) Concerns about adequacy as a helper are also ubiquitous. Most introspective, sensitive psychology majors are all too aware of their own imperfections to be wholly and unconditionally confident about guiding and advising others. In order to address these dual concerns (fear of patients and perceived inadequacy in the helper role), for the past nine years we have been conducting a program at the Pennsylvania hospital that permits specially trained undergraduate volunteers to serve as coleaders and companions within the multifaceted GIT program.

How students learn can be as important as what they learn. A specially designed orientation program emphasizes links between the academic and applied realms. Our results indicate that this program reduces apprehension and empowers students to be more effective in their initial patient contacts. The GIT group process lets students see their instructor applying concepts discussed in the classroom, showing the real-world relevance of research and theory. Sharing extracurricular experience also enlivens class discussions: the students' enthusiastic illustrations of various phenomena highlight the importance of class topics.

Student participants show a steady reduction of patient-related anxiety, an increased awareness of the group's usefulness for patients, and greater perceived self-efficacy. Students learn how to listen and communicate more effectively with challenging patients, to refine interpersonal skills, and to develop greater empathic skills. Interestingly, the personal growth that students report often extends well beyond the clinical setting. After their experience, many say that they see themselves as more "adult," in control, patient, accepting, and loving toward others in general. Several have stated that they saw this program as one of their most influential educational experiences.

Each semester, a new group of enthusiastic students, serving as coleaders and patient companions, bring energy and novel talents and interests into the three tiers of our group program. These student participants have an academic background in psychology and an eagerness to gain practical experience. They are selected on the basis of interpersonal and intellectual skills, and all are highly committed to helping others. Intensive orientation and team building workshops prepare students for situations they are likely to encounter and add to the development of basic helping skills. As students gain experience within the hospital groups, their progress is carefully monitored. Especially capable students are encouraged to continue beyond one semester, and are given increasing amounts of responsibility for organizing group functions.

Since implementation of the GIT approach, staff, patient, and student response has been overwhelmingly positive. Our formal program evaluations have noted the effects on both patient and student participants—objective measures of functioning levels and subjective indicators of satisfaction both attest to the program's success in fostering mutual growth. The longevity of this program is especially noteworthy since this group program functions without any special budgetary support (supplies are usually "found" items or inexpensive materials purchased through leaders' contributions).

Leadership Requirements and Techniques

GIT leaders rely heavily upon their own enthusiasm, warmth, and patience to challenge patients' apathy and resistance to participate in social experiences. Novice leaders should be prepared for a gradual group formation process and considerable patient reluctance at the outset. Coercing participation runs counter to the GIT objective of patient control and choice, and it very rarely works! Group members seem to respond best to respectful invitations to join in, which let patients feel empowered from the outset. Offering appealing, entertaining tasks in a public day hall for a small subgroup of less resistant patients who responded to the initial invitations to participate gives those patients who declined invitations a chance to observe that the group can be a positive, enjoyable experience which is "safe" to try. This seems to make it easier for many patients to risk attending a new, unfamiliar group.

Group leaders also need to be prepared for the slow, gradual change process their patients are most likely to experience. Familiarity with the kinds of program evaluation measures discussed in this manual can give novice leaders a sense of what to expect from patients. Recognizing that for many participants simply attending a therapeutic group on a regular basis is a treatment milestone of sorts can help leaders sustain their own feelings of accomplishment.

The GIT leader serves as a role model in all interactions with other members. Patients observe how leaders respond to interruptions and various inappropriate behaviors, and in so doing learn better ways of responding themselves. We have found it useful when orienting GIT leaders to acquaint them with the basics of different therapeutic approaches. Students can then draw upon different strategies as they see fit. The humanistic, behavioral, and cognitive approaches seem to be most relevant to the GIT setting, however, an understanding of medically based biological treatments of chronic schizophrenia is also critical.

Humanistic Concepts

From the humanistic perspective, leaders

are encouraged to enter the reality of the schizophrenic person, not as a professional but as a fellow human being. Leaders work to build genuine rapport with patient members by communicating concern, respect, and trustworthiness. These leaders respond to members in an accepting, supportive fashion in order to build the patient's self-acceptance and sense of self-worth. By serving as role models of genuineness and authenticity, leaders assist members in the process of becoming more "real" and disclosing to others. Active listening skills, reflection techniques, and communication of empathy form the basis of the helping relationships which unfold within the GIT program. Although the group meetings focus on a structured GIT task, the leaders emphasize relationship-building over task completion. They are willing to meet for informal, nondirective conversations with patient members at the end of group sessions.

The humanistic approach also stresses the importance of patients' forming individualized goals. Leaders help GIT participants reflect on their values and establish personal priorities. The staff helps members revise personal expectations and form reasonable life objectives. This is especially valuable for patients who often feel that they are living in violation of conventional rules and definitions of success. Leaders guide members away from an overvaluation of material things and toward greater appreciation of the beauty of themselves and the world around them.

Behavioral Concepts

The behavioral approach is particularly significant during the early stages of group formation, when managing highly disruptive patients is often difficult. These concepts encourage leaders to recognize how the group environment exerts control over patient behavior. Since the GIT process is aimed at creating and encouraging the use of appropriate behavior, one of the first things leaders do is clarify their specific behavioral expectations for members. Agreeing to participate

in the program represents a behavioral contract—establishing goals such as regular, and punctual attendance, participation in group voting processes, and communication with other GIT members. Leaders discuss the importance of taking turns, listening, and not interrupting others. Once leaders and patients are clear on the behavior "ground rules," feedback is regularly provided. Leaders are taught to use effective approaches to manipulate the reinforcement conditions that operate within the group setting. They are careful to reward appropriate behavior on a consistent basis, and to use ignoring or time out strategies to deal with inappropriate and disruptive behaviors.

The behavioral model of therapy shapes leaders' views of themselves; they are urged to regard themselves as highly influential role models. Because of the importance of observational learning, methods employed by leaders in coping with difficult patients teach onlookers what to do when faced with similar circumstances. The leaders' patience allows others to observe how escalating misbehavior can be prevented. Actual role playing exercises are frequently used within sessions to teach patients assertive ways of managing situations.

GIT groups also help patients acquire new strategies for dealing with the symptoms of their illness. Individuals are taught how to handle distractions, for example, hallucinatory experiences, in an acceptable way. They are also taught how to recognize the signs of decompensation and use methods for reducing stress level. Members are urged to follow all medical recommendations. (The importance of maintaining psychotropic medications is continually stressed for those patients who are likely to be placed on maintenance medication upon discharge.)

The GIT program offers a variety of opportunities for learning, in part because we feel it is important to compensate for all the missed learning opportunities, frequently a consequence of mental illness. Some of the behavioral gaps we see in schizophrenic patients are largely due to their history of progressive social isolation (which often predated their formal diagnosis). Exposing such withdrawn individuals to varied social experiences helps build greater social competence and confidence. Since many patients have spent time in understaffed hospital settings where all too often inappropriate, symptomatic behavior receives more attention that does mature, independent behavior, being part of a GIT group, where therapeutic reinforcement contingencies are carefully maintained, can help to correct previous incidental maladaptive learning.

Cognitive Concepts

The cognitive approach underlies leaders' development of situations in which patients make choices and exercise control. Leaders see the group as a chance to remedy learned helplessness by making patients responsible for group outcomes. Providing appropriate tasks assures a high degree of patient success, which helps to foster greater perceived self-efficacy.

Leaders challenge patients' negative self-concepts and self-defeating negative self-statements. They structure activities to provide concrete evidence of patient competence and ability. Patients begin to think differently about themselves—"I can cook, converse, budget, plan, learn, and make it!" The positive outcome leads to greater generalization of treatment gains and fosters more constructive risk-taking among the patients.

Enhancing Generalization

Once patients embrace the concept of GIT involvement, they must be shown how to apply their learning to other settings. It is important to lay the foundation for transfer of within-group learning to outside involvement opportunities early on in the GIT experience. At initial meetings, leaders should present GIT as a means of developing skills that come in handy in a wide variety of situations. Leaders can point out that the abilities patients will be using within the group are the very same kinds of abilities that many employees use in their jobs, for example, learning to come to group sessions on time without being reminded, developing greater verbal fluency and assertiveness, improving listening skills, increasing writing and drawing skills, and building cooking, gardening, and planning skills. Members can be asked questions about the kinds of activities they might consider pursuing after GIT. Leaders can suggest options and relate anecdotes about previous GIT members who have moved on to sheltered workshops, various kinds of paid employment, and different types of therapeutic involvements. Leaders can ask members to imagine themselves having a regular job, and to envision some of the satisfactions this might provide.

Inviting GIT "graduates" to attend meetings and relate their present activities can motivate members to strive for outside successes. Sometimes encouragement from former peers is more credible to patients than the staff's goading. Keeping track of graduates is well worth the effort. When members are making discharge plans, leaders can have the group secretly prepare a box of personalized, stamped postcards, including a few that have been preaddressed to the GIT group. These cards facilitate communication with former members and remind the departing members of their enduring specialness to group members.

Asking representatives from outside activities (for example, workshop supervisors, occupational therapists, greenhouse directors, boarding home supervisors, etc.) to attend occasional meetings can make these outside activities seem much less threatening. Listening to other patients make commitments to try these outside possibilities makes members less intimidated and in some even stirs up a competitive urge to match the risk-taking of fellow patients. This peer-based motivation can be quite powerful and can overcome considerable resistance to try new things.

Discussing GIT members' outside ventures

within meetings gives leaders the opportunity to reinforce such participation and emphasize the value of expanded involvement with others. Patients making progress can use the GIT session as a forum for relating their new experiences. Having members tell about visits to new places or new therapy group involvements sets the stage for influential role modeling. Often the patient role models are given support from other members. This reaffirms the progressing patients' decision to make forays outside the safe GIT group.

Methods of Staff Support— Avoiding Burnout

The problem of burnout is unfortunately very common among those in the helping professions. Staff members involved with the chronic schizophrenic population are at particular risk of experiencing this debilitating and sometimes paralyzing phenomena.

Burnout involves a downward drift toward physical, emotional, and spiritual exhaustion—a result of chronic high stress and perceived low personal autonomy. The stress usually comes from having to continuously meet people's needs. Efforts to satisfy patients' requests, which at times seem endless and overwhelming, drain staff members' energy and enthusiasm. Burned-out individuals often feel angry and guilty about their loss of enthusiasm and are likely to blame either themselves or the recipients of their help for this drastic attitude reversal.

The experience of pouring in maximal effort for minimal appreciation is extremely taxing and causes erosion of the spirit. During the "burning-out" process, the professional helper has very little concern, sympathy, or respect for the patients. The worker loses enthusiasm, creativity, and commitment. Over time, there is a psychological detachment from patients, and the staff member's attitudes become cynical or negative. Besides

thinking of patients in increasingly derogatory terms, the professional begins to believe that the patients somehow deserve any problems they have—a "blame the victim" orientation. Consequently, service quality deteriorates. Minimal attention and effort is given to each case, and a callous, even dehumanized patient processing takes place. Close, continuous contact with patients involves a chronic level of emotional stress. It is the inability to cope successfully with this stress that is manifested in the emotional exhaustion and cynicism of burnout.

Burnout is experienced by most people to some degree at various times in their life. Its effects upon morale, absenteeism, job turnover, delivery of service, and personal stress and strain are considerable. Once started burnout is highly contagious. Since prevention is much less costly than treatment, steps to avoid burnout among staff are worth taking. We find it helpful to forewarn new GIT leaders about typical job frustrations. We don't minimize burnout, and in fact try to anticipate times when leaders might want to temporarily rotate out of GIT. Periodic assessments to uncover the sources of frustration and monitor their intensity facilitates communication and later problem solving.

We try to discriminate what can be changed from what can't. Offering periodic "vacations" to all GIT members at the end of each treatment module helps to sustain enthusiasm. GIT leaders are given considerable autonomy within the group program, allowing them the opportunity to exercise control. We encourage leaders to care for themselves as well as others. We give them permission to monitor their feelings and express their unmet needs in supervision.

GIT leaders regularly plan specific, realistic goals with defined sub-accomplishments on which to focus. When appropriate, this process includes patient input. We encourage leaders to take pleasure in minor accomplishments and celebrate them along with patient members. GIT leaders must periodically assess their expectations of patients. When possible, the leaders schedule difficult patient groups with more positive experiences. They try to give passive-dependent patients some responsibilities. Leaders also design handouts to convey information that is repeated over and over again.

Some GIT leaders regularly practice one of the following relaxation techniques: progressive relaxation, yoga, meditation, positive imagery, self-hypnosis. They have found that sharing these coping methods with the group members benefits everyone. Since regular exercise is helpful, we urge leaders to intersperse active group tasks with more sedentary ones.

Having multiple GIT leaders creates a support group of colleagues. Leaders can share their problems and receive emotional support. The staff group provides feedback and serves as a reference network in helping to correct unrealistic expectations. GIT leaders provide one another with a needed source of stimulation, information, and advice.

Supervisory Approaches

Supervisory practices can help to prevent burnout and sustain optimal performance. Regular contacts with GIT leaders are needed to give structure and support. Weekly meetings are worthwhile at the beginning, but some leaders may prefer more autonomy. We try to give both positive and negative feedback, emphasizing the positive. Being available to leaders (by phone, if necessary) is helpful. In this way they can be independent but still feel supported. During supervision, it's helpful to ask questions and listen, paraphrase, and reflect leaders' feelings. Try to balance task orientation with emotional support in response to what an employee needs. A common error is giving too much advice, too many direct suggestions and interpretations. Tailoring supervision to individual GIT leader's needs requires practice and effort.

Unfortunately, supervisors are often under enormous pressures themselves. This stress can lead to emotional withdrawal from employees, and less responsiveness to employee needs, more authoritarian and arbitrary approaches, and more critical and less supportive behavior. Supervisors must pace themselves and allow regular breaks in order to avoid burnout themselves.

Patient Selection

Meeting the Needs of Lower and Higher Functioning Patients

Clinical research often provides us with information about how specific, homogeneous patient groups responded to a particular treatment approach. The theoretical reasons why interventions affect varied patient subgroups differently are discussed along with the implication that matching certain approaches to a particular patients is critical.

Unfortunately, in the field we often don't have the luxury of homogeneous patient groupings. Administrative considerations (for example, base unit area or funding source), rather than diagnosis, may be a prime determinant of patient grouping. In addition, the variable, erratic course of mental illness and patient response to medication mean that an individual's functioning level is rarely consistent. Often those with widely dissimilar abilities are found together in a treatment setting. An effective GIT program must flexibly accommodate these varying functional levels. We have developed activities that actually exploit this "problem" by building in ways for higher ability patients to mentor those less competent.

Recruitment

Attracting resistant patients to the GIT program requires warm, enthusiastic leaders with considerable patience. Arranging to conduct initial meetings (see GIT module 1 in Part IV) in a public room with great visibility is a good way to introduce the program to a large number of potential members. In most inpatient settings, there are a few outgoing patients starving for personal attention. These patients are more than willing to welcome a newcomer. Involving a small number of this gregarious-type patient is a way of establishing the first core group, which will serve as an example to other, more reluctant individuals. As the unwilling patients observe this initial group participating in appealing tasks, they'll become more amenable to giving GIT a try. Onlookers can be permitted to approach the GIT task table to see what members are doing. Tasks involving food are usually the most powerful enticement. Leaders can convey reinforcement contingencies which foster appropriate involvement by telling onlookers that refreshments are for group participants. Visitors can be asked if they would like to join the group at its next meeting (or join a new group that the leader wishes to create). To foster positive feelings toward the GIT program, it's a good idea to tell the onlookers that if there is food left over, it will be distributed to them. This limit-setting creates some frustration, but conveys the value placed on group involvement while also communicating the importance of generosity and cooperation. Over time, group members begin to feel "special" when their efforts are recognized.

Since this method of patient recruitment uses "display" GIT meetings as a way of attracting membership, and involves gradually adding new members, a stable group may take a few weeks to develop. Although it is desirable to have all eventual members present from the first meeting on, this is often not feasible with the schizophrenic population. Accordingly, the first three GIT modules use encapsulated tasks, which allow new members to feel a part of what is happening.

Reaching extremely isolated patients re-quires more active efforts. Leaders should make inquiries about such people at staff meetings, and create a target list of the most resistant patients. Involving these individuals will be a slow and gradual process. It is wise for leaders to be aware of this from the outset in order to avoid any undue frustration. Many times pressuring the patient produces extreme oppositional behavior. It is more effective to allow for an initial familiarization period, during which time leaders simply make a point of finding and greeting the individual in a friendly manner. Several weeks of this may be necessary before the patient begins to feel comfortable listening to the leader. Next, offering leftover snacks can be a way of luring the withdrawn person into the meeting room. Eventually the patient begins to check for snacks on his own. When this initiative is taken, it can be socially rewarded or reinforced with refreshments if they are available. Gradually greater involvement in activities can be shaped by making successively greater demands on the withdrawn patient before giving a reinforcement.

Some patients may require one-to-one attention during preliminary meetings. Mute and incomprehensible patients may require individual "interpreters," who can provide them with a mode of communicating with the group ("It seems that Joe would like a..."). This often opens fellow patients' eyes to the needs and "personhood" of a verbally isolated peer. Many times, functionally mute patients do begin to talk within the group, but this can require months of unpressured attention.

Relationship of GIT to Treatment Setting

The Budget Issue — GIT on a Shoestring

Mental health budgets are likely to remain tight, and may even become more so in the coming years. For the past ten years, we have operated our GIT program on a shoestring budget, funded by sporadic volunteer donations. Accordingly, the activities we have developed usually require only inexpensive, readily available materials. We feel that making do with little money in fashioning group tasks provides patient members with valuable lessons in budget-stretching and creativity. Since almost all of our patients will be living on limited funds after discharge, it is important for them to learn how to plan inexpensive leisure activities.

We have also made a careful attempt to emphasize those GIT activity suggestions that require no special facilities (kitchen, greenhouse, etc.) or technical equipment (VCRs, etc.). The tasks described in this guide have been conducted in a standard hospital recreational room without access to special facilities.

Scheduling GIT Meetings

Since GIT emphasizes patients' independence and assumption of responsibilities, group sessions should be scheduled in a way that makes it as easy as possible for members to remember when to come to meetings. It tends to be very difficult for many patients to remember to watch the clock in anticipation of a group session. Integrating meeting times into the rest of the hospital schedule is essential if scheduling conflicts are to be avoided. It also allows other regular activities to serve as cues which can prompt patients' memories and increase punctuality.

Many facilities have a set of morning tasks that have an obvious endpoint. Arranging groups to begin at this time allows leaders to reach patients when they are well rested. Such groups can use the concept of a midmorning "coffee break" as a way of structuring the end of meetings. Afternoon groups which start immediately after lunch also helpfully exploit the client's regular routine to increase the

chances of patient-initiated attendance. In treatment settings where some patients may be involved in outside activities (for example, religious class, recreational outings, music experiences, workshop) during the day, a late afternoon meeting time may be most advantageous. If medications are given out at a set time, planning meetings to immediately follow can be beneficial. Dinnertime can provide a structured endpoint for such groups.

GIT seems to be most effective when patients have the opportunity to meet at least twice a week, for at least a half-hour at each meeting. This makes it easier for patients to remember previous group conversations and activities, and lends greater continuity to the group process. Minimizing the intervals between group sessions also enhances learning. This allows patients to apply their developing understanding of the reinforcement contingencies without long delays. Patients test new behaviors and quickly discover when the consequences are to their liking. Regular meetings also establish and help to maintain momentum and an air of enthusiasm for the group enterprise.

Treatment Planning

The GIT approach is a boon to the treatment planning process because it specifically addresses the often unmet needs of patients who aren't yet ready for more formal therapeutic involvement. Accordingly, resistant patients, who are chronic "nonattenders," can easily be placed within the GIT program. Treatment plan documentation can reflect this genuine attempt to meet the needs of such difficult patients.

The loosely structured GIT format makes it relatively easy to cater to members' changing treatment needs. When specific behavioral problems surface, leaders can often use tasks designed to improve behavior. The routine use of a wide variety of therapeutic tasks allows the GIT leader to be responsive to individualized treatment requirements. Since GIT members are led to expect diversity within meetings, it is not unusual for the task focus to shift from time to time. Specific behavioral needs of one or two members can be targeted, without calling attention to these particular individuals. Such tasks can be presented as general "refresher" sessions.

Use of this GIT manual can streamline the treatment planning process. Goal statements on treatment plans can be readily derived from the therapeutic rationale sections accompanying each sample GIT task. This makes it relatively easy to communicate staff's active involvement in providing planned therapeutic activities on a routine basis. Without such documentation of therapeutic intent, staff efforts can easily go unacknowledged. Without appreciation, staff members are more likely to "burn out" and patients and staff run the risk of seeing the treatment facility as largely custodial.

Evaluating Progress

Measuring therapeutic value for the chronic schizophrenic patient population is a challenge. Many assessment devices designed for other patient groups are insensitive to the slow, gradual changes found in chronic patients. Rapid recovery and discharge are not expected with the chronic schizophrenic patients. Indeed they are partially defined by their resistance to treatment. As a result, gross behavioral measures generally fail to detect growth or improvement signs when administered within a reasonable timeframe. All too often use of such insensitive measures merely confirms negative expectations of "no change" and fosters pessimism among patients and staff alike.

It is important to measure change, however small, within this patient group for several reasons. First, those involved with treatment development and delivery need to know

what works. Only by measuring the slow process of change can treatment techniques be refined. Objective behavioral measures can confirm the staff's impressions of patient improvement and thereby boost therapist enthusiasm. Sometimes objective behavioral measures provide evidence of patient improvement that otherwise would have been overlooked by the staff. This can reduce the risk of staff burnout and provide feedback to therapists about which patient interventions seem to work best.

Second, patients need feedback about their own progress, however minute and gradual. All too often their forward motion goes undetected and unreinforced. These individuals generally lack the obvious behavioral indicators of therapeutic success. Big strides are few and far between. Patients often overlook or minimize the small steps gained—they need to be reminded! Conventional benchmarks of treatment success (going off medication, terminating contact with a therapist, etc.) may be inappropriate for the chronic schizophrenia patients. They may require long-term maintenance medication and ongoing therapeutic support. Developing and sharing sensitive measures of progress during hospitalization helps to maintain patients' motivation and self-respect. They need a way to assess their forward momentum.

Conventional signposts of life success—marriage, living independently, parenthood, steady job, etc.—may also be inappropriate for many of these people. A central therapeutic task with many of these patients involves development of individualized goals. Rewriting their "life script" in light of some of the limitations their illness imposes, for example, rethinking the need to have children, can help these patients recognize their individuality and feel more successful.

Finally, documenting behavioral change is necessary to focus institutional attention on the often forgotten potential of these clients. It is important to underscore the fact that although change for them is often slow, it is not impossible.

Our GIT program assessment approach emphasizes three basic dimensions:

- enhanced participation
- self-efficacy
- social skills

We try to translate these into terms readily grasped by most patients, making the goals of treatment as concrete as possible. The simplicity of this approach permits patients to grasp the group leader's objectives and participate in self-assessments at the end of each 12-week module. Graduations can provide formalized feedback for program participants.

We measure these factors in ways that optimize the opportunity to observe a positive change. Often overlooked signs of patient improvement (for example, arriving on time for group meetings, responding to questions, voicing an opinion, making a suggestion, listening to another member, etc.) are considered worthy of recognition and are recorded for later review by patients, leaders, and other interested staff as well. By keeping track of these molecular behavioral variables, we can sensitively track individual patient experience to provide timely, specific feedback.

We have found that this evaluation method serves as a simplified introduction to the treatment planning process. It seems to be a good way of teaching patients about the overall hospital treatment planning process. By learning to understand, express, and work toward our simple, specific group goals, patients have an easier time interacting with other staff members in team meetings when overall treatment goals are presented and discussed.

Feedback about progress within the group gives these individuals "good news" to share with relatives and visitors. They can convey their pride and their commitment to additional growth, which often fosters greater support, encouragement, and optimism in others.

Sample GIT Groups Format

Tier I: Biweekly afternoon GIT activities groups, open to all floor residents, revolve around structured planned tasks, with considerable weight given to patient suggestions. Choosing a task and giving input on how it will be implemented adds to building perceived self-efficacy and hardiness. Patients develop greater confidence through successful completion of the graded tasks, are supported through frustrating experiences with failure, and are socially reinforced for persistance. The social setting provides ongoing experiences that reinforce regular participation and punctuality, teach social skills, reward interpersonal sensitivity and empathy, and foster a supportive patient network. The large patient group is divided into two or more student-supervised subgroups, so that task difficulty can be matched with the patients' functioning levels and individual attention can be assured. Special patient assistants are designated to perform routine group tasks—preparing and serving refreshments, selecting and distributing supplies, etc.

Tier II: As patients return from dining, a less structured socialization period begins with the after dinner conversation groups. These small groups give members a chance to air feelings and talk about concerns. The groups promote self-acceptance, awareness, reality testing, and sensitivity to others. The leaders assist members to develop reasonable means for solving problems and offer information and clarification when needed. Leaders simultaneously serve as role models for other group participants, whose own listening and helping skills improve as they witness the impact of the leaders' approaches. When a member is disruptive and unhelpful, the leaders' use of patience, behavioral interventions, and diplomatic feedback demonstrates to patients how they might deal with similar disruptions.

In the past when a communal area of interest surfaced in these after dinner groups, future meetings served as a place where members could share and explore the interest. This group experience provides opportunities to share information, to practice developing independent recreational activities, and a chance to build a sense of social belongingness. Patients who have returned after "unsuccessful" experiences within the community benefit themselves and other members anticipating discharge by discussing what they are considering doing differently next time.

Tier III: A living skills group targeting the more highly functional patients meets weekly. This part of the program currently reflects an interdepartmental effort to foster independence and appropriate planning for discharge.

The group utilizes a mixed format including relevant outside speaker presentations, discussions, and many appealing learning tasks—cooking, budgeting, etc.—especially important to those about to be discharged.

Membership in this "high status" group is an incentive for higher functioning patients to continue performing in line with their potential. Membership is a special recognition given patients for their skills and efforts in helping others during the other afternoon groups. Tier III also creates an incentive for other patients to assume greater personal responsibility and plan appropriately for eventual discharge. Communal projects help to foster a cooperative attitude and to reveal the benefits of shared effort. This is particularly important for members who will soon share living arrangements with others.

Part III: Conducting GIT Groups

Starting a GIT Group

How can I get my clients more actively involved in living?

This is the "chronic" question asked by those who care for chronic schizophrenic patients. In consulting with facilities that serve the chronically ill psychiatric patients, it's become clear that caregivers want to be able to do more for these individuals. The helping professionals are not satisfied with simply meeting patients' basic needs. They recognize that custodial care can strip patients of their self-esteem, reinforce passivity and apathy, and create an impersonal, stultifying, and dehumanizing setting that counters therapeutic progress. Caregivers understandably don't want to work in such environments. Many need to see evidence of their patients' psychological growth in order to feel satisfied. Yet many long-term patients frustrate caregivers, because improvement is so slow and resistance to therapeutic overtures so high.

Many chronic schizophrenic patients will not participate in the types of therapeutic programming many institutions provide. These individuals lack the sustained commitment to change required by most formal structured treatment approaches. Because of the illness, side-effects of psychotropic medications, and a history of hospital experiences that result in the "social breakdown syndrome" (Gruenberg, 1974), these people often don't want to do much of anything! They feel overwhelmed by new demands and anticipate failure. They find it hard to experience any enthusiasm and

expect to be bored. They are intimidated by their peers and value isolation. No wonder conventional treatment plans are rarely actualized!

The Group Involvement Training approach was developed to serve the special needs of this resistant patient group. GIT tasks are structured for small groups (five to twelve each, depending on the number of coleaders), and have proven to be cost-effective and to encourage necessary social skills development. The stimulating, dynamic group context is designed to engage even apathetic patients and to accommodate different interests and abilities. The GIT approach is psychologically grounded in social learning theory, emphasizing the importance of building competencies and perceived self-efficacy.

GIT works! The relatively simple tasks have been shown to

- motivate greater patient interest in learning
- increase participation in other, more formal therapeutic programming
- foster individuals' perception of responsibility and improve self-esteem
- encourage development of social skills.

Leading a GIT group does not require extensive expertise; a genuine caring attitude coupled with some basic helping skills are really all that is required. Training paraprofessionals, volunteers, or new staff as group coleaders provides more individualized attention for especially resistant members. GIT tasks assume no special facilities or fancy equipment; a leader can conduct a GIT group in any designated living or recreational area.

The GIT activities described in this program require only inexpensive, readily available materials. Because of the limited attention span of many patients, GIT groups typically meet for a brief period of time—half an hour to one hour—preferably twice a week to assure continuity. Sessions occur in twelve-week modules to guarantee all members a regular, predictable "vacation."

So don't give up on unmotivated patients . . . instead, GIT started and GIT going!

GIT Progress: What GIT Does

How Do Patients Progress With GIT?

The GIT approach to maximizing performance among chronic schizophrenic and other long-term hospitalized patients increases participation levels in activities, the patient's sense of personal efficacy or potential for mastery, and social effectiveness. The modular system provides assorted, stimulating activities which progressively build patient competencies, while allowing for individualized pacing and rapid patient turnover.

Step 1: Participation

A supportive, patient, and respectful approach to these individuals helps make them feel more comfortable with new people. For many patients, fear of failing and painful self-consciousness are powerful obstacles to social involvement. Patients resent being ordered to do things that make them uncomfortable, and have trouble believing that coercive staff members truly have the patient's best interests at heart. Accordingly, GIT members are *not* forced to participate in a set of structured therapeutic activities—it might just overwhelm and frighten them. Instead, members are encouraged to join in an individualized manner designed to increase their sense of options and control. Patients who have been GIT members experience a reduction in their fear of

social learning environments which carries over to many other situations. Once the anxiety obstacle has been surmounted, patients become willing to expose themselves to many learning tasks and opportunities. GIT enhances overall involvement in therapeutic programming. The program promotes active, energetic day-to-day social functioning, increases feelings of group spirit, enhances pride in the treatment facility, and builds enthusiasm. By blending some of the best approaches to chronic schizophrenic patients derived from psychotherapy, and occupational, recreational, art, and music therapies, GIT offers a non-threatening introduction to a wide range of adjunctive treatment modalities, work opportunities, and discharge possibilities. Lower functioning patients are drawn out of their isolation and begin to make more effective use of the institutional resources. Some become ready to plan for discharge to structured community placements. (Prior to GIT this would have seemed far too intimidating to approach openly.) Higher functioning individuals also make more effective use of therapeutic alternatives, and can use the group's support as plans are developed for a more independent future in the community.

Step 2: Efficacy

GIT nourishes personal development and efficacy by building autonomy, practical competence, and confidence. Patients are encouraged to be increasingly self-sufficient and independent, and to assume responsibility for their decisions. Increasing levels of self-direction are fostered by gradually expanding opportunities for individual decisions about group activities. Members learn how to follow regular schedules, to keep appointments, to recognize explicit rules and procedures, and to join in planning activities. GIT orients patients toward preparing for the future. Setting and working toward practical goals are stressed.

Although GIT members are encouraged to become more self-aware, the emphasis of this therapy modality is not on intellectual insight. The GIT group situation provides numerous choices for patients. These opportunities to exert control build a sense of effectance. Flexible, relatively failure-proof tasks reinforce patients' efforts and builds a sense of mastery. GIT increases confidence and motivation for subsequent therapeutic involvements. The program enhances patients' willingness to take appropriate risks necessary for growth. This means greater patient involvement in the hospital treatment planning process (including more assertive behavior that fosters necessary communication) plus more responsibility for discharge recommendations (including taking medications and attending follow-up care) when patients leave the hospital.

Step 3: Social Skills

GIT training gives patients constant practice in relating to others. Observing role models interact effectively teaches necessary skills. Sensitive feedback helps patients refine their social skills. After GIT, patients verbalize more effectively and reveal a deeper understanding of others' needs and reactions. These skills improve satisfaction and functioning levels both within and outside the hospital. The facility's atmosphere improves as patients learn how to apply solutions to problems with other patients. Experienced GIT members are more helpful and supportive toward other patients, creating a more therapeutic climate. Members are usually better able to interact spontaneously with staff and peers, and have learned how to express feelings openly. The shared experiences with cooperative tasks builds a sense of mutual respect and caring, which also fosters a more therapeutic treatment milieu. The improved relationship experiences offer possibilities for learning that can generalize to relationships with family and future roommates, thus improving chances for long-term successful independent functioning.

Individual Progress

Since GIT members are heterogenous, it is hard to make specific behavioral predictions for all GIT participants. What can be said is that *GIT sets the stage for individual growth.* By offering basic but crucial learning opportunities to these often forgotten chronic patients, GIT can help salvage a vast reserve of human talent that would otherwise languish.

Leading GIT: What To Remember

As a GIT leader, you will need to rely heavily upon your own enthusiasm, warmth, and patience in order to challenge patients' fear, apathy and resistance to participate in social experiences. In the beginning leaders should be prepared for a gradual group formation process and considerable patient reluctance. Coercing patient involvement runs counter to the GIT objective of enhanced patient control. Besides, it very rarely works! You will probably find that prospective members respond best to courteous invitations to join voluntarily. This leaves the patient feeling empowered from the outset. It may take more time in the beginning to get a stable group membership this way, but the eventual advantages are well worth it. Members who feel they made the choice to participate

- identify more strongly with group objectives and activities
- resist instructions less
- discover the pleasures of intrinsically reinforcing social experiences.

By presenting appealing tasks in a public room for a small subgroup of less resistant patients, you can gradually attract more participants. The opportunity to sample GIT from afar gives those who at first refused an invitation a chance to see that the group can be a positive, enjoyable experience "safe" to try. This makes it easier for many patients to risk attending a new, unfamiliar group.

Be prepared for the slow, gradual-change process your patients are most likely to experience. For many hospitalized individuals, simply attending a therapeutic group on a regular basis is a treatment milestone. Such an accomplishment can be the vital *first step* that chronic mentally ill patients so sorely need. As a GIT leader, your task is to help mobilize the patient's inner resources that years of failure and boredom have buried. Rekindling hope and enthusiasm for learning may not immediately equip the participants with all the skills needed to feel successful, but it can surely start them on their way.

As a leader, you will serve as an example of how to behave appropriately in all your dealings with patients. GIT members will be watching how you respond to interruptions and disruptive behaviors. Patients will be learning better ways of responding themselves. By sharing your reasoning and decision-making skills with patients, you can help them learn how to relate more effectively in interpersonal situations. Since no leader is perfect, it is important to keep in mind that occasionally admitting your own deficiencies can be very therapeutic for patients. Your willingness to openly confront your failures and try to develop better ways of handling difficult situations demonstrates the value of nondefensive self-appraisal. Furthermore, it allows patients to identify with you more, and to acknowledge the fact that all people fail from time to time. This "normalizing" lesson helps to undo some of the damage associated with members' "mental patient" status.

Therapeutic Strategies

There are many different ways of thinking about therapy. As a GIT leader, you may find it useful to consider some of the basic underlying ideas of different therapeutic approaches.

Familiarity with several strategies will make you better prepared when planning treatment methods for the different group members. You will also be better equipped to deal with the variety of situations likely to arise within the GIT groups you will lead.

There are few "rights and wrongs" in leading a GIT group. The best way to learn what works best for you is to experiment with a few techniques. You can judge their effectiveness by watching how different patients respond. Each time you present a given GIT task, the experience will be unique, because so much of what shapes the group dynamics comes from the individual patients and what they are experiencing on a given day. This can make things a bit unpredictable and demands considerable flexibility on your part, but it also helps to keep things interesting! Feel free to modify suggested tasks as you see fit; you really are the best judge of what your particular group might need.

Humanistic Strategies

From the humanistic perspective, you should strive to establish a close, trusting relationship with members. You will try to relate to patients not so much as a "professional," but as a fellow human being and companion. You can work to build genuine rapport with members by communicating concern, respect, and reliability to patients. By responding to members in an accepting, supportive fashion, you will help to build the patient's self-acceptance and sense of self-worth. By serving as an example of genuineness and honesty, you can assist members in the becoming more "real" and open with others. By listening attentively to members and asking for clarification when needed, you'll communicate respect and caring. This teaches patients how to become more effective listeners themselves.

Although GIT meetings focus on a structured GIT task, in some cases the activity is really a foil for the group's *real* therapeutic agenda: relationship building. The explicit task

- gives patients an excuse for being together
- provides a common basis for conversation
- offers a distraction from interpersonal anxiety.

While task completion does provide for feelings of pride and progress, task performance in many respects is just a means to a larger end. This perspective helps you to remember that group involvement training is most successful when patients learn how to value themselves and others.

The humanistic approach also emphasizes the importance of patients forming individualized goals. You can help patients reflect on their values and establish personal priorities by getting them to discuss their likes, dislikes, and goals. Such discussions can get members to revise personal expectations and formulate reasonable life objectives. This is especially important for patients who often feel that they are living in violation of conventional rules and definitions of success. You can guide members away from an overvaluation of matrial things and toward greater appreciation of the beauty of themselves and the world around them.

Behavioral Concepts

The behavioral approach is significant during the early stages of group formation, when managing highly disruptive patients is often difficult. The behavioral outlook lets you recognize how the group environment exerts control over patient behavior. Since the GIT program is aimed at creating and encouraging appropriate behavior, one of the first things you'll need to do is clarify your specific behavioral expectations for members. Let patients know that you value such things as regular, punctual attendance, participation in group voting processes, and communication with other GIT members. You can discuss the importance of taking turns, listening, and not interrupting others. Once members are clear

on the behavioral ground rules, be sure to provide lots of positive feedback for appropriate behavior. Be careful to reward *good* behavior on a timely and consistent basis, and encourage other members to lavish praise on one another. When patients behave in obviously inappropriate ways, take care not to inadvertently reinforce such behavior by paying a lot of attention to it. Instead, try ignoring or time-out strategies to deal with disruptive behaviors.

The behavioral model of therapy can also be applied by exploiting your value as a role model. Patients learn by watching you, so set a good example! Your patience in dealing with "impossible" outbursts lets patients observe how escalating misbehavior can be prevented. You may want to set up role playing exercises for members to experiment with new ways of behaving.

GIT groups encourage patients to use new strategies for dealing with their illness symptoms. Patients can be taught how to handle distractions, for example, hallucinatory experiences, in a more acceptable manner. You can ask members to "brainstorm"—generate different ideas—about what they can do when they feel they may be hearing things others are not. You can also teach individuals how to recognize the signs of decompensation and suggest some relaxation techniques. Urge members to follow all medical recommendations, especially those patients who are likely to be placed on maintenance medication upon discharge.

The GIT program offers a variety of opportunities for learning, in part because it is necessary to compensate for all the missed learning opportunities that are a frequent consequence of mental illness. Some of the behavioral gaps seen in schizophrenic patients are largely a result of a history of progressive social isolation (which often predated their formal diagnosis). Exposing such withdrawn patients to diverse social experiences helps build greater social competence and confidence. In addition, since many patients have spent time in understaffed hospital settings, where all too often inappropriate, symptomatic behavior receives more attention than does mature, independent behavior, participating in a GIT group can help to correct previous incidental maladaptive learning.

Cognitive Concepts

The cognitive approach recognizes that the behavior of patients is based on their attitudes toward success. If patients expect to fail, they won't try. Providing opportunities for individuals to exercise control and make choices increases patients' beliefs that they can change and make their life more satisfying. You might see your group as a place to remedy learned helplessness and convictions of inevitable failure. To change these negative beliefs, patients should be made responsible for group outcomes. (This includes choosing from GIT tasks — all structured to assure a high degree of success.) Such success helps to foster greater perceived self-efficacy and confidence. You will be challenging your patients' negative self-concepts and self-defeating negative self-statements. By structuring activities that offer concrete evidence of patient competence and ability, you will help members learn to respect their own potential and think differently about themselves, for example, "I can cook, converse, budget, plan, learn, and make it!" This translates to greater generalization of treatment gains and promotes greater constructive risk-taking among patients.

Maximizing Treatment Generalization

One of the big problems in any type of therapeutic or educational endeavor revolves around people's forgetfulness. All too often patients who have been working to master particular skills in one setting seem unable to reproduce their accomplishments elsewhere. Since you want to enable your GIT members to use their newfound abilities outside the group situation, it is important to build techniques for enhancing transfer of learning from the very beginning. Once your patients start to attend GIT meetings on a regular basis and seem to recognize the advantages of social participation, they need to be helped to generalize their learning to other situations.

At initial meetings, you should present GIT as a means of improving skills necessary in many situations. You can mention that the abilities members will be developing within the group are the very same kinds of abilities that many employees must use on their jobs:

knowing how to come to meetings on time without needing to be reminded,
being able to express thoughts and feelings to others in a clear fashion,
listening to what other people have to say and trying to understand their point of view,
knowing how to communicate through simple writing and drawing methods,
feeling comfortable with simple cooking and gardening tasks,
and knowing how to go about planning daily activities.

Since GIT serves as a kind of "stepping stone" to other therapeutic avenues, at the outset of the group you may want to ask members about things they might like to do in the future. Listing some alternatives for them to consider can be a way of opening members up to new possibilities. Sharing anecdotes about previous patients who have moved on to sheltered workshops, different paid employment opportunities, and diverse types of therapeutic involvements can help members identify with possible success and progress. You might ask participants to imagine themselves having a regular job, and to think about what they would like about being employed.

After you have been running GIT groups for some time, you will have an alumni group to draw upon. Occasionally inviting graduates to attend meetings and relate their present activities can serve to motivate current members. Sometimes encouragement from former peers is more influential—present group members can identify more with former patients. Group members know their peer has "been there," and begin to believe that real change is truly possible. Keeping track of graduates is well worth the effort. As mentioned earlier, when members are making discharge plans, it's a good idea to have the group secretly prepare a box of personalized, stamped postcards, including a few that have been preaddressed to the GIT group. This type of going-away present is usually appreciated; it reminds the departing member that he will be missed. As remaining members keep track of the discharged friends, they become desensitized to the idea of leaving the hospital, and become increasingly confident that hard work can pay off.

Another way to increase treatment generalization is to ask representatives from outside activities (for example, workshop supervisors, occupational therapists, greenhouse directors, boarding home supervisors, etc.) to attend occasional GIT meetings. For the patients, this guest program can make these outside ventures and representatives seem much less threatening. Observing other patient members make verbal commitments to try participation in these outside activities creates a momentum of increased involvement and stirs in some a competitive urge to match the achievement. You will probably find that this peer-based motivation can be very powerful and can help members overcome considerable reluctance to try new things.

You can also enhance transfer of GIT learning by reinforcing examples of generalization with verbal praise. Asking members to report on successful outside-group experiences during meetings allows you to applaud the patient's effort and clarify your expectations of greater involvement. Patients who are making progress can use the GIT session as a chance to brag about their successes. Other members are often motivated to try to progress as well. Having members tell about visits to new places or new therapy group involvements sets the stage for imitation. By encouraging other members to support their peer's progress, you can help instill a feeling of pride in one another's accomplishments. To do this, you may want to remind members of how they have worked together to master new skills, possibly suggesting that one member's victories are really victories for the group as a whole.

Part IV: GIT Modules

GIT Modules: How They Work

Each of the five GIT modules contains a diverse array of group activities, balanced to represent different skills areas. A module is designed to provide learning experiences relevant to all three GIT objectives: increased participation, self-efficacy, and social skills. All tasks are structured to maximize patient enthusiasm. Repeated exposure permits patients to rehearse and consolidate their therapeutic gains and use new skills. In this way, the program helps to foster subsequent generalization and transfer of GIT learning to novel situations.

All modules contain twelve assorted tasks requiring a range of patient abilities, and come with suggestions for modifying assignments to suit individual functioning levels. Modules I, II, and III provide entry level experiences appropriate for new GIT participants. Since most facilities have a fair amount of patient turnover, the first three introductory modules are set up so that newcomers can join the GIT group at every thirteen-week interval. Additional members can easily be added after the first twelve-week module concludes and a week's vacation taken by members who will be continuing with the next module. At the end of modules I, II, and III, if the GIT group has grown, membership can be divided. This allows leaders to form more specialized subgroups. One might be a more advanced, more highly verbal GIT group, which would go on to modules IV and V. The other GIT group's members might benefit more from repeating modules I, II, and/or III. Reexperiencing tasks a second time lets GIT "veterans" further develop assignment skills, practice memory skills, and function as teachers and group assistants. Many patients not yet able to progress to more complex therapeutic tasks enjoy the sense of continuity provided by repeating GIT tasks and traditions.

The most advanced modules (IV and V) presuppose prior GIT experience. They offer more verbally challenging tasks which demand a longer attention span, greater concentration skills, and more abstracting abilities. Prior GIT experience with modules I, II, and/or III provides members with the skills and confidence necessary for success at these more frustrating tasks. The tasks included in the advanced modules are designed to prepare group members for eventual discharge.

Most of the GIT tasks described in this manual require two group meetings for completion. Ideally, both sessions should occur during the same week, so that members get a sense of task continuity. Leaders are encouraged to involve members in the activity planning process whenever possible, and to provide time for members to evaluate the success of each task at its conclusion. To allow for the considerable variability among different groups, GIT tasks are presented as continuous units. Leaders can pace themselves and divide coverage of the topic between sessions, as seems most appropriate in their group that week. Should an activity be concluded more rapidly than usual and leave an "extra" session, leaders are encouraged to use this time for supplementary group evaluation of recent tasks and their overall GIT experience. This time can also be used for additional patient planning of upcoming activities.

GIT Module I: Tasks 1–12

1   Membership Invitations

Therapeutic Rationale
Initially, these invitations serve to orient patients to the group process and to convey the emphasis placed on patient control. Colorful, interesting designs attract patient interest. Receiving mail delights and makes the future GIT members feel special, cared for, and included. Group membership and identity begin to crystallize as patients compare notes and realize that others have shared this invitation experience. The invitations give brief, specific

instructions (date, time, and place), which allow patients to initiate participation in an autonomous fashion. Presenting GIT as a voluntary endeavor communicates respect for the person and allows a choice.

Later on, as GIT membership shifts as patients are discharged, the task of making and delivering new invitations as part of a GIT membership drive becomes a way of reinforcing patients' progress. Present members are now recognized as knowledgeable GIT coleaders with responsibility for GIT functions. This task increases patients' social skills development.

Materials
Paper, varied writing and art media
Mass produce the basic invitations by using a copying machine, spirit masters, dittos, or a word processor. Paper quality depends on your budget, but we've found invitations made of inexpensive 8½″ by 11″ bond to be every bit as compelling as rice or fluorescent paper invitations (see sample figure).

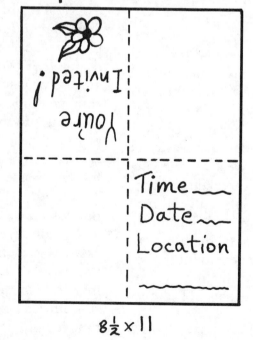

Sample Invitation

You're Invited!

Time ___
Date ___
Location ___
___

fold on dotted lines

$8\frac{1}{2} \times 11$

Task 1

Procedures

Lower Functioning Patient Activities
• suggest design or select from possible design themes
  • fold pages to create cards
  • cut and paste mini-collage designs
  • crayon black and white designs
  • make finger or potato print designs
  • use adhesive tape or sticker designs
  • engage in supervised delivery of invitations to new members

Higher Functioning Patient Activities
• conduct a group selection of design themes (A patient can volunteer to moderate/lead group in this shared decision-making process.)
  • practice communicating, cooperative compromising
  • individually decorate invitations using a variety of media (Patients can generate a list of media preferences and can help obtain the necessary supplies. As the leader, emphasize creativity and originality, for example, making ink prints from found objects, leaves, etc., or using glitter, pasting photograph and magazine cutouts, etc.)
  • take part in the group final design selection process for the invitation
  • plan and implement delivery of invitations

2   Introductions and Identification Tags

Therapeutic Rationale
This introductory activity helps members get acquainted with peers and group coleaders in a relatively structured, nonthreatening manner. It addresses the patients' problems of social withdrawal and isolation by minimizing the anxiety that motivates this defensiveness. The task is relatively simple and intentionally not beyond the ability of any group member. It provides patients with structured guidelines that offer reassurance and limits.

Components of the activity are solitary, so that patients won't feel overwhelmed by too many demands to interact with others in the beginning. The concrete, sensory motor aspect of the task allays anxiety about deficient interpersonal skills. This phase sets the stage for reality testing by presenting tangible evidence of the external world and its response to patients' actions. Comments from other group members provide consensual validation for each member.

The latter part of this activity promotes verbal interaction among members, makes the leaders' expectations of greater social interaction explicit, and sanctions increased interpersonal communication. Giving patients clear permission to talk to one another can help break down the norm of silence that dominates many hospital wards.

This activity also makes members more aware of their own individuality. Preparing identification tags that are uniquely the patient's own reinforces a sense of identity and distinguishes the self. Sharing personal identification information and receiving positive feedback for such disclosure can enhance self-esteem and increase sharing. Patients learn that social and verbal interactions can be rewarding, gain others' approval, and help overcome feelings of loneliness.

Wearing the identification tags accentuates the distinctions among individuals while underscoring members' ability to share in and contribute to a collective activity. This diminishes members' fears of losing a tenuous sense of self if they dare to join in communal activities.

Materials
name lists
blunt end scissors
construction paper (different colors)
markers, pens, pencils, and crayons
masking tape
stickers of various kinds (optional)

Procedure

Colorful materials can be laid out on the table ahead of time in order to stimulate members' interest and draw in new participants. You can explain that to get acquainted all group members will begin by making their own name tag. Ask members to pick out a piece of construction paper the color they want to use. Distribute scissors and ask members to cut out any shape they'd like for their name tag. Patients can be supported throughout, with comments reflecting their actions (for example, "Mary, you decided to try blue") and affirming their choices ("that's an interesting shape").

After members have completed the first step, ask them to select a marker or crayon and write their names. Encouraging higher functioning patients to assist those members who may be unable to write helps establish the group theme of cooperation and mutual effort. Finally, have members use a piece of tape to affix their identification tags onto their clothing. Again, more able members can serve as role models and assistants for the less competent members.

When everyone has completed a name tag and is sitting around the table, you can ask questions about each person's name:

— Do you happen to know how you got that particular name?
— Were you named after anyone in particular?
— Does your name reflect your ethnic background?
— Did you pick your name at confirmation?
— Do you use a nickname?
— If you could change your name, what would you like to be called?

Be sure to ask only one question at a time and to point out and reinforce any commonalities between patient's names:

— Both of your names begin with the same letter!

— Both of you were named after your grandmothers.
— Both of you use nicknames.

Discovering such commonalities helps to counteract the patient's feelings of being alienated and different from others.

You can then offer to tell the group about the meanings of their first names, by referring to the lists about names.

Lower Functioning Patient Activities

• Discussing the origin of each person's name may tax some patients' ability to sustain attention and relate to one another. Therefore a more simplistic and active technique may be required. After making name tags, the group leader can ask all individuals whose names fall within specific categories to stand.

Categories
names begin with a specific letter
name tag is a particular shape
name tag is a particular color
name written in a specific color
ends with the same letter
uses a nickname

In using this approach, it is important to provide everyone an opportunity to stand with another group member.

• The opportunity to make choices needs to be limited to avoid overwhelming very low functioning patients. This can be accomplished by limiting the choice to two options—necessary for increasing the involvement. Rather than asking patients if they want to make a name tag, ask if they want to use a blue or red pen to write their names.

• Name tags can be precut, using a variety of colors and shapes.

• If all patient members are unable to write their names, the group leader can do it after the patient has chosen a name tag and a marker.

• Various stickers can be added to already prepared name tags.

Higher Functioning Patient Activities

Some more capable members may want to read the name lists on their own, and should be encouraged to do so. Encourage a discussion of members' favorite names: what they mean, what positive associations make these names "favorites," for example, "I had a good friend named Sue when I was little." Members can discuss current popular names and name "fads" from their youth (for example, "Have you ever noticed how many Debbys and Lindas were born in the late 40s, early 50s? . . . I wonder why so many parents picked those names back then . . . "). Discuss the advantages and disadvantages of having a popular name ("Everyone knows how to spell common names . . . but it's tough when five people in a room all have the same first name.") Since many individuals with low self-esteem don't like their names, saying something positive about everyone's name can be helpful.

Female Names

A

Name	Meaning	Derivation
Abigail	Source of delight	Hebrew
Ada	Happy	Saxon
Adabel / Adabelle	Happy and fair	Teutonic-Latin
Adah	An ornament	Hebrew
Adalia	Noble	Teutonic
Adela	Cheerful; shining bright	Saxon
Adelaide	Beautiful princess	Saxon
Adele	See Adela.	
Adine / Adina	Delicate	Hebrew
Adria	Unknown	Latin
Adrienne	Artful	Latin
Agatha	Good	Greek
Agna	A diminutive of Agnes.	
Agnella	An Italian form of Agnes.	
Agnes	Pure	Greek
Agneta	A Swedish form of Agnes.	
Aileen	Light	Greek
Ailsa	Noble and of good cheer	Teutonic
Aimee	Beloved	French
Airlia	Ethereal	Greek
Alanna / Alane	Comely; fair	Celtic
Alda	Rich	Teutonic
Aldercy	Chief or prince	Old English
Aldis / Aldys	From the house	Old English
Alethea	Picturesque	Greek
Alexa	A diminutive of Alexandra.	
Alexandra	Helper of mankind	Greek
Alexis	Helper	Greek
Alice / Alicia / Allis / Alyce / Alys	Noble and of good cheer	Teutonic

Name	Meaning	Derivation
Alina	Comely; fair	Celtic
Alison	Of sacred flame	Teutonic
Allegra	Sprightly; cheerful	Old French-Latin
Alma	Fair; good	Latin
Alodie	Wealthy; prosperous	Anglo-Saxon
Aloys / Aloyse	Famous in war	Teutonic
Alta	Wholesome	Teutonic
Althea	Dainty; graceful	Greek
Alvina	Beloved by all	Teutonic
Alvita	Vivacious; animated	Latin
Alysia	Captivating	Greek
Alyssa	Noble; of good cheer	Teutonic
Amabel	Lovable	Latin
Amara	Unfading	Greek
Amaris	Whom God hath promised	Hebrew
Amaryllis	Fresh; sparkling	Greek
Amber	A jewel	Arabic
Amelia	A worker	Teutonic
Amethyst	A precious stone	Greek
Aminta	Desirous of making spiritual things practical	Uncertain
Amity	Friendly	Latin
Amorette	Little love, or sweetheart	Latin
Amorita	Beloved	Latin
Amy	Greatly beloved	Latin
Andrea / Andreana	Feminine forms of Andrew.	
Angela / Angelica	Angelic	Spanish-Teutonic
Angeline	Sweet messenger	French
Anita	Assertive	Spanish
Ann / Anna	Gracious	Hebrew / Swedish
Annabel	A heroine	Hebrew
Anne	See Ann.	

Name	Meaning	Derivation
Annette	Elfish; exquisite	French
Antoinette	Incomparable	French
April	"Sun and flowers"	Latin
Araminta	Lofty	Hebrew
Ardath } Ardith	Rich gift	Anglo-Saxon
Ardra	Ardent; eager	Latin
Aretina	Virtuous	Greek
Ariana	Silvery	Welsh
Ariella	Ethereal	Hebrew
Arlana } Arlena } Arlene	A pledge	Celtic
Arlinda	Associative and adaptable	Uncertain
Astred } Astrid	Impulsive in love	Teutonic
Atalaya	A watch tower	Spanish-Arabic
Atalie	Pure	Swiss
Atlanta	Beautiful, swift-footed huntress	Greek
Audrey	Golden	English
Audris	Fortunate; wealthy	Teutonic
Augusta	Imperial; exalted	Latin
Aurelia	Golden; beautiful	Latin
Avice	Refuge	Latin
Azalea } Azalia	Spared by Jehovah	Hebrew

B

Name	Meaning	Derivation
Bab	A dependable alluring personality	Uncertain
Babetta	Little enchanter	Italian
Barbara	Shy	Latin
Beatrice	Blessing	Latin
Becky	The ensnarer	Hebrew
Bee	A 'pet' name for Beatrice.	
Belinda	Shining; bright	English
Belle	Beautiful	French
Benita	The blessed	Latin
Bernadette	French diminutive of Bernard.	
Bertha	Bright	Teutonic
Bertilde	Commanding battlemaid	Teutonic
Beryl	A jewel	Hebrew
Bessie } Beth } Betty } Betsy } Bett } Bette	See Elizabeth.	
Beverly	From Beverley, a town in Yorkshire, England	Old English
Bianca	White; fair	Teutonic-Latin
Biddy	Zealous over her own	Uncertain
Billie	Feminine nickname from William.	
Blanche	White; fair	French
Blenda	Dazzling; glorious	Teutonic
Blossom	A modern name carrying its own suggestion.	
Brenda	Feminine form of Brand.	

Name	Meaning	Derivation
Bridget	Strong	Celtic

C

Name	Meaning	Derivation
Candice	Glowing	Latin
Carlotta	Noble birth	Spanish
Carol	Song of Joy	Old French
Caroline	Noble-spirited	Teutonic
Carrie	A diminutive of Caroline.	
Cassandra	Inspiring love	Greek
Catherine	Pure	Greek
Cecile	Lover of harmony	Latin
Charlotte	Noble-spirited	Teutonic
Cheryl	A feminine form of Charles.	
Christine	Christian	French
Claudia	Dazzling	Latin
Colette	A necklace	French-Latin
Cynthia	Belonging to the moon	Greek

D

Name	Meaning	Derivation
Daphne	Shy; fleet	Greek
Dara	The heart of wisdom	Hebrew
Darice	Queenly	Persian
Darlene } Darline	Tenderly beloved	Anglo-Saxon
Daryl	Beloved; dear	Old English
Davina	The beloved one	Hebrew
Dawn	The break of day	Anglo-Saxon
Day	Creatively active	Uncertain
Deanna	Bright as day	Latin
Deborah	Industrious	Hebrew
Decima	The tenth	Latin
Deirdre	Sorrow	Gaelic
Delia	Shining; bright	Celtic
Della	A form of Delia.	
Delora	From the seashore	Latin
Deloris	A form of Delores.	
Demetria	A form of Demeter, the Greek Goddess of harvests.	
Denise } Denice } Denys	Feminine forms of Dennis	
Desma	A pledge or bond	Greek
Devona	The defender	Anglo-Saxon
Diamond	Priceless	Uncertain
Diana	Goddess; perfect	Latin
Dinah } Dina	Judged; vindicated; avenged	Hebrew
Dione } Diona	Daughter of heaven and earth, in Greek mythology.	
Dixie	Girl from the South.	
Dolly	Diminutive of Dorothy.	
Dolores	Sorrowful	Spanish
Donella	Little mistress	Latin
Donna	Lady	Latin
Dora	A gift	Greek
Dorcas	Gazelle	Greek
Doria } Dorea	Forms of Doris.	

Name	Meaning	Derivation
Doris	The sea	Greek
Dorothy	} God-s gift	Greek-Teutonic
Dorothea		

E

Name	Meaning	Derivation
Echo	A nymph, in Greek mythology.	
Edana	Ardent; fiery	Celtic
Eden	Delightful; pleasant	Hebrew
Edith	} Tall; stately	Teutonic
Editha		
Edna	Capricious	Teutonic
Effie	Of fair fame	Greek
Eileen	Light	Greek
Elaine	Bright	Greek
Elberta	Responsible; trustworthy	Teutonic
Eleanor		
Eleanore	} Light	Greek
Elinor		
Elise	Gracious and ambitious	Uncertain
Eliza	Faithful	French
Elizabeth	God's promise	Hebrew
Ella	Sprightly	Greek
Ellen	See Eleanor.	
Eloise	Dreamy; romantic	French
Elsie	Mirthful	Saxon
Elvira	Impartial; fair	Latin
Esmerald	Ideality brilliantly made practical	Uncertain
Emily	Artistic	English
Emma	Energetic	English
Emmeline	Intellectual	English
Enid	Self-confident; quiet	Celtic-Latin
Erina	Girl from Ireland	Celtic
Erna	Intent on purpose	Teutonic
Ernestine	Earnest	Teutonic
Esmerelda	Bright hope	Spanish
Essie	} A star	Latin
Estelle		
Esther	Good fortune	Persian
Ethel	Noble	Teutonic
Etta	Home ruler	Teutonic
Eudora	Good, or delightful, gift	Greek
Eugenia	Well-born	Spanish
Eunice	Victorious	English
Euphemia	Accomplished	Greek
Eva	Life; giver of life	Hebrew
Evadne	Faithful unto death	Greek
Evangeline	Angel-like	Greek
Eve	See Eva.	
Eveline	Pleasant	Gaelic
Evelyn	Hazelnut	Latin

F

Name	Meaning	Derivation
Faith	Sure reliance	Teutonic
Fanchon	Free	Teutonic
Fanny	} Diminutive forms of Frances.	
Fannie		
Faustine	Lucky	French

Name	Meaning	Derivation
Fay		
Fae	} Fairy	Old French
Faye		
Fayette	A form of Fay.	
Felice	} Happiness	Latin-French
Felicite		
Fern	A feather	Greek
Fidelia	The faithful	Latin
Fifi	Diminutive of Josephine.	
Fiona	White; fair	Celtic
Fleur	A flower	French-Latin
Fleurette	Little flower	French
Flora	Flowers	Latin
Florence	Flourishing	Latin
Floy	Genial; productive; beloved	Uncertain
Fonda	Profound; well-based	Spanish-Latin
Frances	Free	Teutonic
Fredericka	Rich peace	English
Fritzi	} Peaceful ruler	Teutonic
Fritzie		
Fulvia	Blonde; yellow-haired	Latin

G

Name	Meaning	Derivation
Gail	} Abounding joy	Old English
Gale		
Garnet	Forcefully voicing her ideals	Uncertain
Gay	Light-hearted; merry	French-Teutonic
Genevieve	Humble	French
Georgette	Feminine form of George.	
Georgia	} Womanly dignity	English
Georgiana		
Geraldine	Affectionate	English
Germaine	Exquisite; lovely	French
Gerry	The ambitious life of the party	Uncertain
Gertrude	All truth	English
Ginger	Gaining poise and power	Uncertain
Gladys	Demure; capable	Welsh
Glenna	From the glen or valley	Gaelic
Gloria	The glorious	Latin
Grace	God's blessing	English
Greta	A pearl	Greek
Gwen	Intellectual, with	
Gwendoyln	understanding	Celtic
Gwynne	} White; fair	Celtic
Gwyn		

H

Name	Meaning	Derivation
Hannah	Good	Hebrew
Harriet		
Hatty	} Mistress of the home	Teutonic
Hattie		
Heather	Flowering heath	Modern
Hedda	Robe	Anglo-Saxon
Helen	Light	Greek
Henrietta	Of noble birth	English
Hesper	Evening star	Greek
Hester	Good fortune	Persian

Name	Meaning	Derivation
Hetty	A star	Persian
Hilda	Strong; merciful	Teutonic
Holly	A name from the shrub, holly	Anglo-Saxon
Hope	Hope	Teutonic
Hortense	Fragrant; sweet	French

I

Name	Meaning	Derivation
Ianthe	Delightful	Greek
Ida	Happy	Teutonic
Idette	A form of Ida.	
Idola	Industrious; constant worker	Teutonic
Ilka	Industrious	Teutonic-Latin
Imogen / Imogene	Pity for all who need	English
Ina	Pure	Greek
Inez / Ines	Pure; gentle; meek	Greek
Inga	Daughter	Teutonic
Ingrid	Daughter	Teutonic
Irene	Serene; peaceful	Greek
Iris	The rainbow	Greek
Isabel / Isabella	See Elizabeth.	
Iva	A short form of Ivana.	
Ivana / Ivane	God's gracious gift	Hebrew
Ivy	A name from the vine, ivy	Teutonic

J

Name	Meaning	Derivation
Jacinta	Lovely; beautiful	Greek
Jacqueline	The supplanter	Hebrew
Jane	God's grace	Hebrew
Janet / Janella	Forms of Jane.	Modern
Janel	Darling Jane	Gaelic
Janice	An elaborated form of Jane.	
Jean	Loving Jane	Gaelic
Jeanette	Little Jane	French
Jeanne / Jenny	See Jean.	
Jennifer	White wave	Celtic
Jerry	Forceful; erratic	Modern
Jessica	The Lord's grace	English
Jessie	My present	Gaelic
Jill	See Julia.	
Jo	See Josephine.	
Joan	Gift of the Lord	English
Jocelyn / Jocelin	Merry or jocund	Latin
Josephine	A reward	French
Joy	Delight	Old French
Joyce	Winsomely lovely	English
Judith	Praise of the Lord	Hebrew
Judy	Short for Judith.	
Julia / Juliet	Volatile; changeable	Latin-English
June	Youthful	Latin

Name	Meaning	Derivation
Justa / Justina	Just	Latin

K

Name	Meaning	Derivation
Kara / Karen / Karin / Karena	Pure	Greek
Kate / Katherine	Pure	Greek
Kathie	Short for Katherine.	
Kathleen	Dear to my heart	Celtic
Kay	Exultant; rejoicing	Greek
Kerry	One who through experiences discovers the law of change	Modern
Kirstie	The Christian or anointed	Greek
Kit / Kitty	Nicknames for Katherine.	
Koren	Maiden	Greek

L

Name	Meaning	Derivation
Lalita	Artless; straightforward	Sanskrit
Lana	Light	Greek
Lara	Famous	Latin
Laura	A laurel; famous	Latin
Laurel	Victorious	Latin
Laurice / Loris	The laurel	Latin
Lea / Leah	The weary	Hebrew
Lenore / Leonora / Leonore / Lenora	Light	Greek
Leonie	The lion	Latin
Leora	Light	Greek
Leslie / Lesley	From the gray fort	Celtic
Leta	Joy	Latin
Letitia / Letty	Glad	Latin
Liane / Liana	A bond	French-Latin
Libby	Consecrated to God	Hebrew
Lilia	A form of Lillian.	
Lillian	Pure as a lily	Latin
Lily	Pure	English
Lilybell	Fair lily	Latin
Linda	Beautiful	Latin
Lise / Liza	Consecrated to God	Hebrew
Lois	A short form of Louise.	
Lola	A diminutive form of Charlotte.	
Lolita / Loleta	Elaborated forms of Lola.	
Lona	Single; alone	Middle English
Loretta	Pure	Spanish

Name	Meaning	Derivation
Lorna	Stately	Uncertain
Lotus	A name from the flower, lotus.	
Lou	A diminutive of Louise.	
Louise	Beautiful; yielding	French
Lucette	A coquette	Uncertain
Lucia	Lustrous	Latin
Lucille	Shining	French
Lucinda	Brilliant	English
Lucy	See Lucille.	
Lulu	Wolf	Latin
Luna	Shining	Latin
Lupe	Light	Teutonic
Lydia	With a good mind	Greek
Lynn / Lynna	A cascade	Anglo-Saxon

M

Name	Meaning	Derivation
Mabel	Histrionic	English
Madeline / Madeleine / Madelaine / Madelene / Madelena / Madalyn	The tower	Hebrew
Madra	Mother	Latin
Mae / May	Maiden	Middle English
Manda	Lovable	Latin
Mara	The original Hebrew form of Mary.	
Marella	Little Mary	
Maretta / Marette	Shorter forms of Marietta.	
Marian / Marion	Forms of Mary	Old French
Maribel	Beautiful Mary	Hebrew-Latin
Marice	A form of Mary.	
Marie	The French form of Mary.	
Marietta	Italian and French	
Mariette	diminutives of Mary.	
Marilynn	Gay; popular	Uncertain
Marjorie / Marjory / Margery	A pearl	Greek
Marla	A Bavarian form of Mary.	
Marlene / Marlena	The tower	Hebrew
Marta	Lady; mistress	Aramean
Martha	Resigned	Hebrew
Mary	Sympathetic	Hebrew
Matilda	Courageous	English
Maud / Maude	Gift of the Lord	English
Maureen	The dark	Latin
Maurita	Dark	Latin
Mavis	The song thrush	Celtic
Maxine	The greatest	Latin
Mazie / Maisie / Meg	A pearl	Greek
Melinda	Grateful	Saxon

Name	Meaning	Derivation
Merle	A blackbird	Latin
Meryl / Meriel	Variants of Muriel.	
Mildred	Teasing	English
Millicent	Comforter	English
Monica	An advisor	Latin
Muriel	Myrrh	Arabic

N

Name	Meaning	Derivation
Nancy	Grace	Hebrew
Naomi	Sweet; pleasant	Hebrew
Natalie	Christmas child	Latin
Nora	Honorable	Celtic
Norma	Model	Latin

O

Name	Meaning	Derivation
Octavia	The eighth	Latin
Olga	Holy	Teutonic
Opal	named after the gem	Latin
Oriole	Golden thrush	Latin
Orlene	The golden	Latin

P

Name	Meaning	Derivation
Pamela	All honey	Greek
Patricia	Noble; well-born	English
Paula / Paulette / Pauline	Little	Latin
Pearl	Tearful	English
Peony	A name from the flower, peony.	
Pepita	A Spanish diminutive of Joseph.	
Persephone / Persis	A weaver of dreams; author	Greek
Philana	Lover of mankind	Greek
Philippa	Lover of horses	Greek
Phyllis	Coy	English
Polly	See Mary.	
Pollyanna	Compound of Polly and Anna	Modern
Poppy	A name from the flower, poppy	Old English-Latin
Portia	Successful pleader	Latin
Primrose	A name from the flower, primrose	Latin
Priscilla	Dutiful; neat; lovely	Latin
Prudence	Careful; quaintly pretty	English
Psyche	The soul	Greek

R

Name	Meaning	Derivation
Rachel	Motherly	Hebrew
Ramona	Wise protector	Teutonic
Rana / Raina	Royal	Sanskrit
Ray / Rae	Female deer	Scandinavian
Reba	A short form of Rebecca.	
Rebecca	A troth or peacemaker	Hebrew
Regina	Queenly	Latin

Name	Meaning	Derivation
Renita	Firm; self-poised	Latin
Rita	A pearl	Greek
Riva	A dreamer	Old French
Roberta	Of shining fame	Teutonic
Robia	Sensitive to needs of humanity	Uncertain
Rosa	}	Latin
Rosalie	}	French
Rosalind	} A rose	English
Rosamond	}	English
Rose	}	English
Rosanna	} Rose of grace	Latin-
Rosanne	}	Hebrew
Rosemary	Unspoiled	Latin
Roxana	} Dawn of day	Persian
Roxanne	}	
Ruby	Red	English
Rue	A name from the plant, rue.	
Ruth	Friendly	Hebrew

S

Name	Meaning	Derivation
Sadie	} Diminutives of Sarah.	
Sallie	}	
Salome	Enticing	Greek
Sandra	Helper of mankind	Greek
Sarah	A princess	Hebrew
Sharon	Harmonious; musical	Uncertain
Shirley	From the white meadow	Old English
Sibley	Related; friendly	Anglo-Saxon
Sibyl	} Wise, prophetic	Greek
Sibil	}	
Sidra	Starlike	Latin
Sigrid	Expression of sadness; understanding	Uncertain
Silva	Woodland maid	Latin
Silver	White	Anglo-Saxon
Simona	Heard	Hebrew
Sirena	A siren	Greek
Sonja	}	
Sonia	} Wisdom	Greek
Sonya	}	
Sophia	Wise	Greek
Stella	A star	Latin
Stephania	} Loyal	Greek
Stephanie	}	
Sue	}	Danish
Susan	}	Hebrew
Susie	} Trusting	Danish
Suzette	}	French
Sylvana	Forest maiden	Latin
Sylvia	A forest nymph	Latin

T

Name	Meaning	Derivation
Tallula	A place name	Modern
Tamara	The palm tree	Hebrew
Tara	Tower	Gaelic
Teresa	} Generous giver	Italian
Thalia	}	Greek
Terry	Dramatically individual	Uncertain

Name	Meaning	Derivation
Theodora	} Divine gift	Greek
Theodosia	}	
Theresa	} Harvester; reaper	Greek
Therese	}	
Titania	Sweetness; intuition; eminent ability	Uncertain
Tonia	Beyond praise	Latin
Trista	The sorrowful	Latin
Trixy	She who blesses	Latin

U

Name	Meaning	Derivation
Ula	Jewel of the sea	Celtic
Una	The one	Latin
Undine	Daughter of the waves	Latin
Urania	The heavenly	Greek
Ursula	Even-tempered	Latin

V

Name	Meaning	Derivation
Val	Valorous; strong	Latin
Valeria	Worthy	Teutonic
Vania	God's gracious gift	Hebrew
Veda	Knowledge; understanding	Sanskrit
Velma	Warm-hearted	Teutonic
Vera	Faithful	Slavonic
Verna	Spring-born	Latin
Vicki	Versatile in inspirations	Uncertain
Victoria	Conquering	Latin
Vida	Life	Hungarian
Viola	} A name from the flower, violet	Old French-
Violet	}	Latin
Virginia	Innocent	Latin
Vivian	Lively	Latin

W

Name	Meaning	Derivation
Wanda	The wanderer	Teutonic
Wileen	Resolute protectress	Teutonic
Wilhemina	Practical	English
Willa	The desired	Anglo-Saxon
Wilma	Reserved	Uncertain
Wilmet	A diminutive of Wilhemina.	
Winifred	} Idealistic	English
Winnie	}	
Wynne	White; fair	Celtic

X

Name	Meaning	Derivation
Xanthe	The yellow-haired	Greek
Xantippe	Shrewish	Greek
Xenia	Hospitable	Greek
Xylia	Of the wood	Greek
Xylina	Of the wood	Greek
Xylona	Guards; directs; protects; revives	Uncertain

Y

Name	Meaning	Derivation
Yedda	Discipline through fine and applied art	Uncertain

Name	Meaning	Derivation
Yola	Bespeaking the beauty of quietude	Uncertain
Yolanda	A name from the flower, violet.	
Yvette	The archer	Scandinavian
Yvonne	The archer	Scandinavian

Z

Name	Meaning	Derivation
Zandra	Helper of mankind	Greek

Name	Meaning	Derivation
Zaneta	God's gracious gift	Hebrew
Zenda	Womanly	Persian
Zenia	The hospitable	Greek
Zillah	Restful	Hebrew
Zita	The harvester	Greek
Zoe	Flight; freedom	French
Zora } Zorah }	Dawn	Slavonic
Zorana	An elaborated form of Zora.	

Male Names

A

Name	Meaning	Derivation
Aaron	A mountain; a tower of strength	Hebrew
Abner	Paternal	Hebrew
Abraham	Tall; father of a multitude	Hebrew
Absolom	Peace loving	Hebrew
Achilles	Taciturn; sympathetic	Greek
Adam	Red earth; lover of outdoors	Hebrew
Addison	Descendant of Adam	Uncertain
Adelbert	Mentally brilliant	Teutonic
Adrian	Pessimistic; hard to please	Latin
Ahern } Ahearn }	Lord of the horses	Celtic
Alan	Cheerful; in harmony	Celtic
Alban	Pure	Latin
Albert	Firm; responsible	Teutonic
Alexander	Leader of men	Greek
Alexis	Helper	Greek
Alfred	Kingly	Teutonic
Algernon	Prosperous	French
Alison	Of holy fame	Teutonic
Allen	See Alan	English
Allister } Alaster }	Variants of Alexander	Gaelic
Alonzo	Ready; willing	Greek
Aloysius	Grace	Latin
Alton	From the old manor or village	Old English
Alvin	Beloved of all	Teutonic
Ambrose	Immortal	Greek
Amery } Amory }	Industrious	Teutonic
Amos	Strong, courageous	Hebrew
Andrew	Manly	Greek
Anthony } Antonio } Antony }	Inestimable; incomparable; praiseworthy	Latin
Archibald	Holy prince; extremely bold	Teutonic
Armand	Public spirited	French
Arno	Eagle	Teutonic
Arnold	Strong as an eagle	Teutonic
Arthur	High-minded	Celtic
Aubrey	Ruler of the elves	Teutonic
Auburn	Fine appearing; delicately constituted	Uncertain

Name	Meaning	Derivation
August	Venerable	Latin
Augustus	Exalted; imperial	Latin
Austin	Useful	Latin

B

Name	Meaning	Derivation
Bailey } Baylen }	Bailiff or steward	Old French
Baird	Bard or minstrel	Celtic
Baldwin	Friendly; bold	Teutonic
Barlow	Dweller on the bare hill	Old English
Barney	Tendency to reform	Uncertain
Barrett	Bear-like	Teutonic
Barry	Straightforward	Celtic
Bartholomew	Warlike son	Hebrew
Basil	Royal	Greek
Baxter	Baker	Old English
Benedict	Blessed	Latin
Benjamin	A surety	Hebrew
Bernard	Bold as a bear	Teutonic
Bert	Bright	Teutonic
Bertram	Fair; illustrious	Teutonic
Bing	Intuitive adaptation	Uncertain
Blaine	Thin or lean	Celtic
Blake	Either black or pallid, according to the root-word chosen	Old English
Bob	See Robert.	
Boris	Warrior	Slavonic
Boyd	Yellow-haired	Celtic
Bradley	From the broad meadow	Old English
Brady	Sensitive; quick; variable	Uncertain
Brand	A fighter	Uncertain
Brant	Firebrand	Teutonic
Brent	From the steep hill	Old English
Brett	A Breton or native of Brittany	Celtic
Brian	Strong; sincere	Celtic
Bruce	Positive; daring	Gaelic
Bryant	Strong	Celtic
Buck	Unpremeditated in direct action	Uncertain
Byron	From the cottage	Teutonic

Name	Meaning	Derivation

C

Name	Meaning	Derivation
Cadwallader	Valiant in war	Saxon
Caesar	Purposeful	Latin
Caleb	A dog lover	Hebrew
Calvert / Calbert	Herdsman	Old English
Calvin	Bold	Latin
Cameron	Crooked nose	Celtic
Carl	Forceful	Teutonic
Carlisle / Carlyle	From the walled city	Old English-Latin
Carlos	Expressive; colorful; fastidious	Uncertain
Carroll / Carrol	Champion	Celtic
Carter	Cart-driver	Old English
Cary / Carey	From the fortress	Celtic
Casey	Valorous	Celtic
Caspar	Gift-bearer	Saxon
Cecil	Harmony	Saxon
Chadwick	From the warrior's town	Old English-Celtic
Charles	Manly	Teutonic
Chester / Cheston	Dweller in a fortified town	Old English
Christopher	Whimsical; humorous	Greek
Chuck	Quick; hasty; efficient; adaptability	Uncertain
Clarence	Bright; illustrious	Latin
Claude	Affectionate	Latin
Clay	Man of clay, or mortal	Teutonic
Clayton	From the town on the clay bed	Teutonic
Clement	Merciful	Latin
Clifford	Valorous	Saxon
Clifton	From the farm at the cliff	Old English
Clinton	From the headland farm	Teutonic
Clive	Cliff dweller	Old English
Clyde	Heard from afar	Welsh
Colburn	Cool; using good judgment	Uncertain
Colby	From the black farm	Old English
Colman / Coleman	Dove	Irish
Columbus	Curious	Greek
Conan	Capable in research; quiet; adroit	Uncertain
Conrad	Optimistic; resolute	Teutonic
Coolidge	Careful and protective	Uncertain
Cornelius	Studious; noble	Latin
Corwin	From the enclosed land, or court	Anglo-French
Craig	Crag-dweller	Scotch
Crosby	Dweller by the town cross	Teutonic
Curt	Short or little	Latin
Cyril	Lordly	Greek
Cyrus	Jolly	Persian

D

Name	Meaning	Derivation
Dale	Dweller in the dale	Teutonic
Dan	A Judge	Hebrew
Daniel	A Judge	Hebrew
Darrell	Beloved or dear	Old English
Daryl	Beloved or dear	Old English
David	Beloved	Hebrew
Dean	From the valley	Old English
Dennis	A worshipper	Greek
Dick	See Richard.	
Dirk	Dark or lord	Celtic/Latin
Donald	Proud; a chief	Celtic
Douglass	Thoughtful	Celtic
Duncan	Brown chief	Celtic
Durand	A lasting friend	Latin
Dwight	White; fair	Teutonic

E

Name	Meaning	Derivation
Earl	Nobleman or chief	Anglo-Saxon
Edgar	Wealthy	Teutonic
Edward	A guard	Teutonic
Eli / Elias	Faithful to God	Hebrew
Eliot / Elliott	Forms of Elias.	
Emil	Industrious	Teutonic
Eric	Princely	Teutonic
Ernest	Serious; earnest	Greek
Eugene	Well-born; noble	Greek

F

Name	Meaning	Derivation
Felix	Happiness	Latin
Fillmore	Perceiving the intangible and the factual	Uncertain
Floyd	The gray	Celtic
Ford	Productive; practical; prophetic	Uncertain
Forrest	Woodland dweller	Anglo-Latin
Franchot	The free	Teutonic
Francis / Frank	Dutiful	Teutonic
Franklin	A freeman or free-holder	Teutonic
Fred / Frederick	Peaceful ruler	Teutonic

G

Name	Meaning	Derivation
Gabriel	Fights for the right	Hebrew
Gail / Gale	Gay or lively	Old English
Galen	Unknown	Greek
Garland	Crowned for victory, or garlanded	Old French
Garner	Protecting warrior	Teutonic

Name	Meaning	Derivation
Garrett	Mighty with the spear	Teutonic
Gaylord	Particular; prideful; original	Uncertain
Gene	Gifted; energetic; sympathetic	Uncertain
Geoffrey	Chivalrous; brave	Teutonic
George	One who amasses a fortune	Greek
Gerald	Affectionate; jolly	Teutonic
Gerard	Brave with the spear	Teutonic
Gideon	A deliverer	Hebrew
Gilbert	Progressive	Danish
Giles	Shield-bearer	Greek
Glen / Glenn	Of the glen or valley	Gaelic
Goddard	Divinely firm	Teutonic
Godfrey	Quiet	Teutonic
Gordon	Generous	Gaelic
Grant	Great	Latin
Gregory	Watchful	Greek
Griffith	Having great faith	Latin
Grover	Dweller in the grove	Old English
Guthrie	War serpent	Celtic
Guy	A leader; sensible	French

H

Name	Meaning	Derivation
Hal	See Henry.	
Halbert	A gentleman	Gaelic
Hale	Robust	Teutonic
Hamilton	From the beautiful mountain	Norman
Harlan / Harland	From the land of warriors	Teutonic
Harold	Unafraid; a warrior	Teutonic
Harrison	Noble; princely	Saxon
Harry	See Henry.	
Harvey	Bitter	Celtic
Hector	Defender	Greek
Henry	Home ruler	Teutonic
Herbert	Gay	Teutonic
Herman	Satisfied	Teutonic
Hiram	Nobly born	Hebrew
Holman	From the river island	Teutonic
Holmes	Son of Holman.	
Homer	Secure	Greek
Horace	Light of the sun	Latin
Horatio	Worthy to be beheld	Latin
Howard	Aggressive	Saxon
Hubert / Hugh / Hugo	Intellectual	Teutonic
Humphrey / Humfrey	Prop, or supporter, of peace	Teutonic
Hyman	A variant of Hyam, meaning life	Hebrew

I

Name	Meaning	Derivation
Ian	A scotch form of John.	
Ingram	Ing's raven. Ing was a mythical Scandinavian hero	Teutonic
Ira	Descendant	Hebrew

Name	Meaning	Derivation
Irvin / Irving / Irwin	Friend of the sea	Anglo-Saxon
Isaac	Mirthful; glad	Hebrew
Isadore	A good gift	Spanish
Ivan	A Russian form of John.	

J

Name	Meaning	Derivation
Jack	See John.	
Jacob / James	The supplanter	Hebrew
Jarvis	Keen as the spear	Teutonic
Jasper	Master of many treasures	Persian
Jay	The quick or lively	Old German
Jed	Beloved of the Lord	Hebrew
Jeffrey	God's peace	Teutonic
Jerel	Expert in colorfully adapting concepts	Uncertain
Jeremy / Jerome / Jerry	Exalted; placed high above others	Hebrew
Jesse	Wealthy	Hebrew
Jock	See John.	
Joel	Strong-willed	Hebrew
John / Jonathan	Given by God	Hebrew
Jordan	The descender	Hebrew
Joseph	An addition	Hebrew
Jules	A French form of Julius.	
Julius	Kind	Latin
Justin	Just	Latin

K

Name	Meaning	Derivation
Karl	See Charles	Swiss
Kay	Strong; determined	English
Keane / Keene	Sharp, tall, handsome	Old English
Keith	Wood-dweller	Welsh
Kelby	From the farm by the spring	Teutonic
Kelly	Impetuous though gentle and helpful	Uncertain
Kelsey / Kelcey	Dweller by the water	Teutonic
Kendall / Kendal	From the bright valley	Celtic
Kenneth	Handsome; quick	Gaelic
Kent	White or bright	Celtic
Kerry / Keary	The dark	Celtic
Kilby	From the farmstead by the spring	Teutonic
Kim	Chief	Welsh
Kirk	Dweller by the church	Teutonic
Kit	Short for Christopher.	

L

Name	Meaning	Derivation
Laban	White	Hebrew

Name	Meaning	Derivation
Lamar	Forward; cooperative; capable	Uncertain
Lambert	His country's brightness	Teutonic
Landry	Ruler of the place, or local magnate	Saxon
Lang	Long or tall	Teutonic
Latimer	Acutely conscious of the world's needs	Anglo-French
Lawrence	Victorious	Latin
Lawton	From the hillside farm	Old English
Lee	Physician	Celtic
Leighton	From the meadow farm	Old English
Leland	From the meadow land	Old English
Lemuel	Dedicated to God	Hebrew
Leo		Greek
Leon	Lion-like	French
Leonard		Teutonic
Leopold		Teutonic
Les	Artistically expressing	Uncertain
Leslie	From the gray fort	Celtic
Lester	Seeking the truth	Saxon
Levi	A bond; a tie; a promise	Hebrew
Lewis	Seeking fame	Teutonic
Lincoln	From the settlement by the pool	Celtic-Latin
Lionel	Lion-like	Latin
Llewellyn	Lightning	Welsh
Lloyd	Indecisive; gray	Celtic
Louis	See Lewis.	

M

Name	Meaning	Derivation
Macy	Enduring material	Uncertain
Magnus	Great	Latin
Malcolm	Kingly	Latin
Mallory	Ill-omened	Old French / Latin
Manus	Determined though able to change	Uncertain
Manvil / Manvel	From the great estate	Latin
Marcus / Mark / Marc	Defender	Latin
Mario	Martial. From Mars the Latin god of war	Italian
Marshall / Marshal	A marshal	Old French
Martin	Unyielding	Latin
Marvin / Marwin	Famous friend, or sea-friend	Teutonic
Matthew	Gift of the Lord	Greek
Maurice	Persistent	Latin
Max	Going ahead; a leader	Latin
Maxwell	Dweller by the spring	Anglo-Saxon
Maynard	Mightily brave	Teutonic
Meredith / Meridith	Protector from the sea	Celtic
Merrell / Merrill	Famous	Teutonic
Michael	"Like to God"	Hebrew

Name	Meaning	Derivation
Milburn	From the millstream	Old English
Miles	A soldier	Celtic
Milton	Colored red	Greek
Mitchell	A form of Michael.	
Montague	Of the peaked mountain	Latin
Morgan	Born by the sea	Celtic
Morley	From the meadow on the moor	Old English
Morrell / Morel	Swarthy	Latin
Morris	Moorish or dark-skinned	Latin
Mortimer	Ever living	French
Morton	From the farm on the moor	Old English
Moses	Drawn out of the water	Hebrew
Murdock	Prosperous seaman	Celtic
Murray / Murry	Seaman	Celtic
Myron / Myreon	Fragrant	Greek

N

Name	Meaning	Derivation
Napoleon	Lion from the forest	Greek
Nash	Alert; active	Uncertain
Nat	Versatile and innately refined	Uncertain
Nate	Delicate variation in productivity, a word painter	Hebrew
Nathan / Nathaniel	A gift	Hebrew
Neal / Neil / Neill	A champion	Celtic
Ned	Diplomatic	Uncertain
Nelson	Son of Neal	Celtic
Neville	From the new town	Latin
Newlin / Newlyn	From the new spring or pool	Celtic
Newton	From the new estate	Anglo-Saxon
Nicholas	Victory of the people	Greek
Nigel	Dark	Latin
Niles	A form of Nicholas	Finnish
Noah	Restful	Hebrew
Noel	Christmas	French-Latin
Nolan / Noland	Noble, or famous	Celtic
Norbert	Brightness of the sea	Teutonic
Norman	Hopeful	Teutonic
Norris	Man from the North	Teutonic
Norton	From the north village	Anglo-Saxon
Norward	Guardian of the northern road or gate	Teutonic

O

Name	Meaning	Derivation
Oakes	The oak	Old English
Oakley	From the oak tree meadow	Old English
Obadiah	Servant of the Lord	Hebrew
Octavius	The eighth born	Latin
Ogden	From the oak tree valley	Old English
Olaf	Relic, or reminder, of his ancestor	Old Norse

Name	Meaning	Derivation
Olin Olen	} Derived from Olaf.	
Oliver	Dutiful; peaceful	Saxon
Omar	Material research for academic heights	Uncertain
Ordway	Warrior with spear	Anglo-Saxon
Orin Oran	} White of skin	Celtic
Orlando	Handsome	Italian
Orson	The bear	Latin
Orville	Emotional; artistic; serene	Saxon
Osborn	Divinely strong	Teutonic
Oscar	Active	Celtic
Osric	Divine ruler	Teutonic
Oswald	Power of God	Saxon
Otis	Keen of hearing	Greek
Otto	Rich	Teutonic
Owen	Well-descended	Saxon

P

Name	Meaning	Derivation
Paige	Helpful; pride of ancestry	Uncertain
Paine Payne	Man from the country or a rustic	Latin
Palmer	Palm-bearer	Old English-Latin
Parker	Keeper of the park	Old English
Pascal	Pass over	Hebrew
Patrick	Noble; patriotic	Latin
Paul	Little; small	Greek
Paxton Paxon	} Traveling trader	Teutonic
Payton Paton Peyton	} Diminutive forms of Patrick	Scotch
Pedro	A Spanish and Portuguese form of Peter.	
Pembroke	From the headland	Old Welsh
Penn	Constructively, curious and cultured	Uncertain
Percival Percy	} A knight; piercing eye	Latin-Saxon
Perrin Perren Perryn	} See Peter.	
Perry	The pear tree	Old English
Peter	Reliable; dependable; a rock	Greek
Phelan	Wolf; anciently, the wolf was a highly respected animal	Celtic
Philip	A lover of horses	Greek
Pierce Pearce Peirce	} Forms of Peter	Anglo-French
Pierpont Pierrepont	} Dweller by the stone bridge	French-Latin
Pierre	The usual French form of Peter.	
Pierson Pearson	} Son of Pierre or Peter.	
Pollard	Cropped haired	Teutonic

Name	Meaning	Derivation
Porter	Keeper of the gate	Latin
Powell	Alert	Celtic
Prentice	An apprentice or learner	Latin
Prescott	From the priest's dwelling	Old English
Preston	From the domain of the church or priest	Old English
Putnam	Dweller by the pond	Anglo-Saxon

Q

Name	Meaning	Derivation
Quincy	From the place owned by the fifth son	French-Latin
Quinn	The wise	Celtic

R

Name	Meaning	Derivation
Raleigh	From the deer meadow	Old English
Ralph	Home-loving; hero	Saxon
Randal	House wolf	Teutonic
Ray	Kingly	Old French
Raymund	Wise protector	Teutonic
Reginald	Kingly	Teutonic
Richard	Stern, but just	Teutonic
Robert	Winning over all	Teutonic
Robin	A form of Robert made famous by Robin Hood.	
Roger	Tall; straight	Teutonic
Roland	Adventurous	Teutonic
Ronald	Worthy	Saxon
Roy	Kingly	Saxony
Rudolph	Unconquerable	Teutonic
Russell	Red-haired, fox-like	Latin
Rutherford	From the cattle ford	Old English
Ryan	A capable executive	Uncertain

S

Name	Meaning	Derivation
Salisbury	From the fortified stronghold	Old English
Sam	See Samuel.	
Samson Sampson	} Like the sun, or resplendent	Hebrew
Samuel	Asked of God	Hebrew
Sanborn	From the sandy brook	Old English
Sanders Saunders	} Helper of mankind	Greek
Sandon	From the sandy hill	Old English
Sanford	From the sandy ford	Old English
Sargent	An officer, squire, or military attendant	Old French-Latin
Saul	Asked for	Hebrew
Saville Savill	} From the window farm	Old French-Latin
Sawyer	A cutter of timber	Celtic
Schuyler	A shelter	Dutch
Scot Scott	} The wanderer	Scotch
Seabrook	From the brook by the sea	Old English
Searle Serle Serlo	} Armed, or wearing armor	Teutonic

Name	Meaning	Derivation
Seaton } Seton }	From the place by the sea	Old English
Seaver	Victorious stronghold	Anglo-Saxon
Selby	From the manor farm	Teutonic
Selwyn	Palace friend	Anglo-Saxon
Seth	The appointed	Hebrew
Seward	Guardian of the sea	Anglo-Saxon
Sewell	Mighty in victory	Teutonic
Seymour	Famed at sea	Teutonic
Shaw	From the shady grove	Old English
Shelby	From the ledge farm	Anglo-Saxon
Shelley	From the ledge meadow	Anglo-Saxon
Sherard	Of splendid valor	Anglo-Saxon
Sheridan	Irish nickname meaning the wild man	Celtic
Sherlock	Fair-haired	Old English
Sherman	A shearer or cutter	Old English
Sherwin	Eminent is friendship	Anglo-Saxon
Sherwood	From the bright forest	Old English
Sibley	Friendly	Anglo-Saxon
Sidney	Bruised; trouble	Saxon
Siegfried	Liberated	Teutonic
Sigmund	Victorious protection	Teutonic
Silas	See Silvanus.	
Silvanus } Sylvanus } Silvester } Sylvester }	Forest dweller	Latin
Simeon	A servant of the Lord	Hebrew
Simon	Obedient	Hebrew
Simpson } Simson }	A Swedish form of Samson.	
Sinclair	The illustrious	Latin
Sloan } Sloane }	Warrior	Celtic
Sol	The sun	Latin
Solomon	Peaceful	Hebrew
Spencer } Spenser }	The dispenser of provisions	Old English-Latin
Sprague	Alert; lively	Teutonic
Stacey } Stacy }	Stable or dependable	Latin
Stafford	From the landing ford	Old English
Standish	From the stony park	Old English
Stanfield	From the stony field	Old English
Stanford	From the paved ford	Old English
Stanhope	From the rocky hollow	Old English
Stanislaus	Glory of the camp	Slavonic
Stanley	Dweller at the stony sea	Old English
Stanton	From the stone dwelling	Old English
Stanway	Dweller by the stone highway	Old English
Stanwood	From the stony wood	Old English
Stephen	Loyal	Greek
Sterling } Stirling }	Of honest value	Old English
Stewart } Stuart }	A steward	Anglo-Saxon
Stillman	Gentle	Anglo-Saxon
Stilwell	From the still spring	Anglo-Saxon
Stoddard	Keeper of horses	Old English

Name	Meaning	Derivation
Sumner	A summoner	Old French-Latin
Sutton	From the south village	Old English
Swain	A youth	Teutonic

T

Name	Meaning	Derivation
Taber	Herald	Old French
Tait	Cheerful	Scandinavian
Talbot	See Taber.	
Taylor	A tailor	Old French-Latin
Teague	Poet	Celtic
Tearle	Stern	Old English
Ted } Theodore }	Divine gift	Greek
Tedman } Tedmund }	Protector of the nation	Teutonic
Terrence } Terence } Torrance }	Soft or tender	Latin
Terrill } Tirrell }	Martial ruler	Teutonic
Tertius	The third	Latin
Thaddeus	The praised	Hebrew
Thatcher } Thacher }	A roofer, or thatcher	Old English
Thaxter	See Thatcher.	
Thayer	Of the nation's army	Teutonic
Theodoric } Theodric }	Ruler of the people	Teutonic
Theron	Hunter	Greek
Thomas	Good company	Hebrew
Thornton	From the thorn-tree farm	Old English
Thorpe	From the small village	Teutonic
Thurlow	From Thor's (Norse god of war) hill	Old English
Timothy	Honoring God	Greek
Tony	Beyond praise	Latin
Tracey	Courageous	Anglo-Saxon
Trevor	Prudent	Celtic
Tyler	Maker of tiles	Old English

U

Name	Meaning	Derivation
Ulysses	One who adventures far	Greek
Upton	From the high town	Anglo-Saxon

V

Name	Meaning	Derivation
Valentine	Strong; valorous	Latin
Vernon	Flourishing	Latin
Victor	Conquering	Latin
Vincent	Invincible	Latin
Vladimir	World-ruler	Slavonic

W

Name	Meaning	Derivation
Walt } Walter }	Of great destiny	Teutonic

Name	Meaning	Derivation
Warren	Protecting friend	Teutonic
Washington	Purifying	Saxon
Wayland	From the land by the highway	Old English
Wayne	A wagon-maker	Old English
Webster	Weaver	Old English
Welby	From the farm by the spring	Scandinavian
Weldon	From the spring by the hill	Teutonic
Wellington	From the prosperous estate	Anglo-Saxon
Wells	Dweller by the springs	Old English
Wendell / Wendel	Wanderer	Teutonic
Wesley / Westley	From the west meadow	Old English
Weston	From the west village	Old English
Weylin	Son of the wolf	Celtic
Whitby	From the white dwellings	Scandinavian
Whitney	From the white island	Anglo-Saxon
Wilbur	Inventive; constructive	Anglo-Saxon
Wildon	From the wooded hill	Old English
Wilfrid / Wilfred	Resolute for peace	Teutonic
Will	Short for William.	
Willard	Protecting	Saxon
William	Resolute	Teutonic
Willis	Son of Will.	
Wilmer / Wilmar	Beloved and famous	Teutonic
Wilmot	Beloved heart	Teutonic
Wilson	Son of Will.	
Wilton	From the farmstead by the spring	Old English
Winchell	Drawer of water	Anglo-Saxon
Windsor / Winsor	At the bend of the river	Teutonic
Winfred / Winfrid	Friend of peace	Teutonic
Winslow	Friendly	Anglo-Saxon
Winston	Friendly stone	Old English
Winthrop	From the friendly village	Teutonic
Wirt	Worthy	Anglo-Saxon
Woodley	From the wooded meadow	Old English

Name	Meaning	Derivation
Woodrow	From the hedgerow by the forest	Old English
Woodward	Keeper of the forest	Old English
Worden	Guardian	Old English
Worthington	From the riverside	Anglo-Saxon
Wright	Workman	Anglo-Saxon
Wyatt / Wiatt	Guide	Old French
Wylie	Beguiling	Anglo-Saxon
Wyman	Warrior	Anglo-Saxon
Wyndham	From the windy village	Old English
Wynne	Intuitive; quiet; sympathetic	Uncertain

X

Name	Meaning	Derivation
Xaver	One who protects the rights of others	Uncertain
Xavier	Brilliant	Arabic
Xenos	A worker in that which exalts	Uncertain

Y

Name	Meaning	Derivation
Yardley	From the enclosed meadow	Old English
Yates	Dweller by the gates	Old English
York	A sacred tree	Celtic-Latin

Z

Name	Meaning	Derivation
Zaccheus	Pure	Hebrew
Zachariah / Zachary	Whom God remembers	Hebrew
Zebedee	A blessing	Hebrew
Zed	A scientific example of rejuvenation	Uncertain
Zel	A follower of a sacred art	Uncertain
Zelos	A noble leader in philosophical circles	Uncertain
Zenas	God's gift	Hebrew

3 Making Fruit Salad

Therapeutic Rationale

This task teaches patients the value of cooperative effort and to follow simple directions. Each member contributes to a communal project and therefore learns to share responsibilities. Enjoying the salad at the end of the meeting reinforces persistence and patience.

Materials

ripe fruit (different types)	spoons
	cups
dull knives	paper towels
large bowl	

Use any kind of fruit you wish (ripe fruit permits use of dull knives, although the juice gets a bit messy). Watermelon, peaches, and bananas are good choices for groups that include members with denture problems.

Procedure

In advance, suggest to patients that you thought it would be a good idea to have something cool and refreshing like a fruit salad. Discuss the nutritional advantages of such foods and the need for dietary fiber. Ask members what kinds of fruit they would like to have in the salad.

When you get the fruit, ask each member to cooperate by cutting up one type of fruit into bite size pieces.

Have them put all the fruit in one big bowl and ask a patient to mix it. Have another member serve it to the others.

Lower Functioning Patient Activities
1. suggest types of fruits to use
2. put fruit in bowl
3. mix fruit
4. serve fruit

4   Woodblock Sanding

Therapeutic Rationale

This simple tactile activity is a relaxing way for members to become comfortable with the notion of group involvement. The task is straightforward and virtually failure-proof, permitting members to converse during the activity. Sanding wood can be a sensual experience, which reinforces members for listening to directions. This task requires patients to make some basic tactile discriminations, leading to development of greater attention to detail. Members must make some simple judgments, which can increase confidence in decision-making ability. Discussing possible uses for the sanded blocks of wood is an exercise in creativity. This activity also provides experience with materials some may later encounter in the workplace.

Materials

box of assorted rough lumber pieces (scrap pieces from a construction site or lumber yard can provide an assortment of sizes and shapes)
rough and fine grain sandpaper
optional: gloves; wood stain or water color; shellac, polyurethane, or varnish; disposable paint brushes; wood glue

Procedure

Ask a group assistant to distribute pieces of rough and fine sandpaper to all members. Then, ask participants to select a block from the box containing the assorted lumber scraps. A leader can demonstrate how to use the sandpaper or ask a member with some experience in working with wood to demonstrate his or her sanding technique. Mention to members that they may want to be careful not to get wood splinters (gloves can be provided for patients unable to take precautions). Ask patients to start with the rougher grade of sandpaper, and then use the finer paper after preliminary sanding is complete. When patients make the decision to move on to the finer sandpaper, leaders can support their decision by agreeing with their timing judgment. After completing their first block of wood, ask members if they'd like to begin work on another block. If they say no, suggest that they sit and relax after putting out such a big effort. Patients may want to resume work after a brief rest.

After everyone has completed the sanding they choose to do, members can feel one another's blocks and offer feedback. The members can discuss possible wood constructions for the group to consider assembling at a future meeting. A free-form sculpture, wall hanging or mobile is an easy communal construction project. Participants may want to stain or paint, and subsequently shellac their blocks.

5   Rooting Plant Cuttings

Therapeutic Rationale

This activity provides patients with immediate, concrete reinforcement for following simple directions. It provides an opportunity to develop or refine basic measuring skills, and offers practice in interpreting visually presented instructions. Members enjoy creating their own "instant" plants and are later rewarded for reliably caring for their cuttings when they discover new plant growth and roots! If participants decide to combine their efforts and create one large communal group plant, their cooperative effort is reinforced when they see their impressive collective plant. Later, when additional individual cuttings can be taken from this large plant, members will be thrilled to realize that (thanks to the regenerative ability of certain plants) this project allowed them to contribute to the group without forfeiting their own plant.

Materials

styrofoam or clear plastic cups
perlite
large parent plant, for example, a wandering
    jew, which provides robust, quick-grow-
    ing cuttings
pencils
blunt scissors
measuring cup and spoons
instructions diagram

Procedure

Group members fill individualized foam cups (which can be decorated ahead of time) with perlite, using a standard measuring cup. Next, they moisten the rooting medium with six tablespoons of water. Patients are taught to cut plant sections above nodules and to remove extra stem portion and unnecessary leaves (see diagram). Participants can use pencils to poke holes in perlite mixture and then insert and secure the cuttings. A schedule for regular watering and misting is established. Later, individual cuttings are transferred to a large communal pot. Additional individual cuttings are taken from a new large plant later on. This entire process can be repeated at regular intervals. Cuttings make fine gifts for friends and staff, and can even be sold to help defray costs of supplies.

6   Butterfly Designs

Therapeutic Rationale

This task is simple enough so that a majority of the patients are able to complete it with relatively little assistance. When patients gain enough confidence in their abilities to create somewhat realistic butterflies, some can help the more disabled with this craft. The activity permits open conversation and increases self-confidence.

Materials

colored tissue paper   scissors and tape
pipe cleaners   wire hanger (optional)
colored stickers

Procedure

Members choose color of tissue paper and if able cut a sheet of paper approximately 4″ by 7″. The paper is gently gathered at the center and a pipe cleaner is folded in two and placed over the gathered portion of the tissue paper. The expanded ends of the pipe cleaner are twisted and shaped into the form of antennas; stickers may be placed in the "wings." Members may want to combine their individual butterflies to make a mobile by attaching them to a wire hanger.

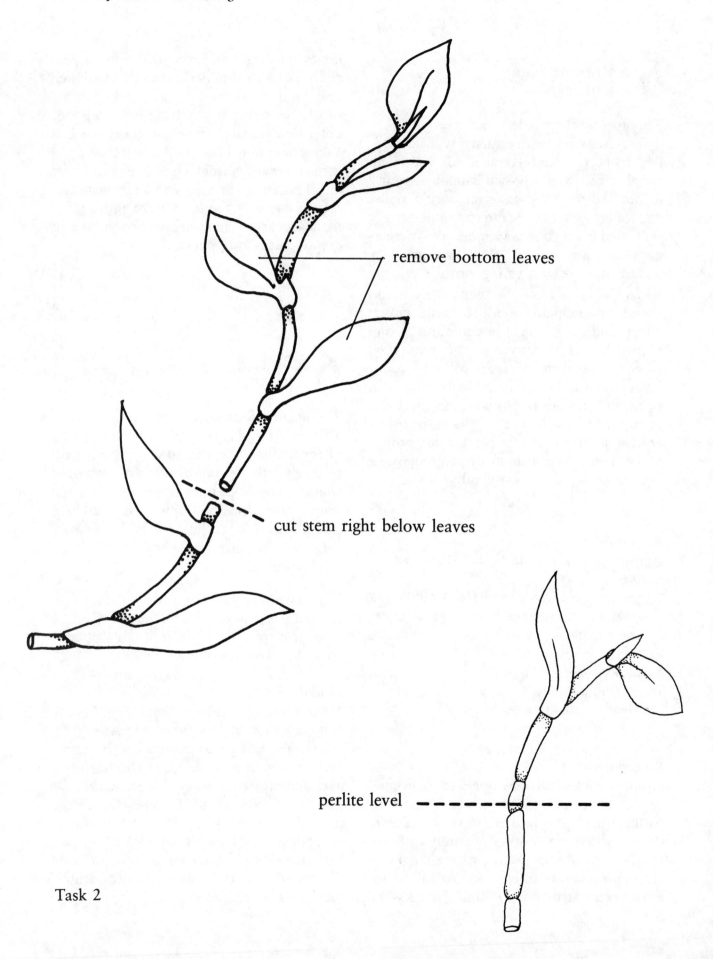

remove bottom leaves

cut stem right below leaves

perlite level

Task 2

7 Music: Listening and Rating

Therapeutic Rationale

Patients are often socially withdrawn, flattened in affect, nonresponsive, and generally inattentive to environmental stimuli. This activity, using a taped medley of popular country and rock music, is designed to produce positive feelings and facilitate social interaction. Patients are asked to sing, hum, or dance along with the music, and to respond to a simple questionnaire assessing their feelings about the tape.

Participation in the activity assists members in forming an identification with the other participants and develops communication skills. In order to complete the exercise, members must pay attention to you and to each other, thereby dealing with social reality. It also helps patients to relax, thus reducing anxiety.

Materials

tape recorder
prerecorded tapes (include a mixture of rhythms and types of music)
questionnaire (see sample)
pencils

Procedure

Gather the group together in a corner of the room. Ask for a volunteer group assistant to operate the tape recorder. Ask members to try to agree on the recorder's volume. Play the tapes and encourage members to participate in any way they feel comfortable (singing, nodding, swaying, clapping, dancing, humming, etc.). Toward the end of the meeting, while certain selected tapes are playing ask patients to describe their feelings and reactions to the music by completing the questionnaire. Have members discuss the similarities and differences among their reactions.

8 Holiday Decorations

Therapeutic Rationale

Preparing simple holiday decorations fosters temporal orientation and builds community spirit. Hanging or displaying various symbols of different holidays provides tangible evidence of group involvement and draws attention from staff and other patients. These decorations enliven the environment and provide visual interest and variety.

Easter Egg Decoration

Decorating Easter eggs is a colorful and different project. It boosts everyone's spirits. The task requires *responsibility, patience, communication, cooperation, creativity,* and *decision-making skills* on the part of the patients. Because of the fragile nature of eggs, patients have the *responsibility* of not breaking the eggs or spilling the dye. In order to get a dark colored egg, the participants must be *patient* while waiting for the dye to work. Their patience is also tested when they have to wait to use the dye colors they choose, for the dyed eggs to dry, and to eat the eggs (the dyed eggs can be refrigerated; egg salad can be prepared for the next meeting). *Communication* and *cooperation* are enhanced because they are encouraged to share the different dye colors. *Creativity* is reinforced through attention given to the way in which they decorate their eggs with the wax crayon, the dye, the stickers, etc. Finally, the patients make a *decision* about when to remove the egg from the dye by testing its color every so often and deciding when they consider it to be an optimal shade. This exercise in subjective judgment lets members reveal mutual respect and tolerance of individual differences.

Materials

3 dozen eggs, hard boiled
commercial dye kit (includes dye, stickers, etc.)

Music Rating Questionnaire

Name:_____

Date:_____

Song #1:
1. Did you enjoy this music? _____
_____
2. Was this music FAST or SLOW? _____
_____
3. Was this song LOUD or QUIET? _____
_____
4. Did this music make you feel HAPPY or SAD? _____
_____
5. Did this music make you want to DANCE or RELAX? _____
_____

Song #2:
1. Did you enjoy this music? _____
_____
2. Was this music FAST or SLOW? _____
_____
3. Was this song LOUD or QUIET? _____
_____
4. Did this music make you feel HAPPY or SAD? _____
_____
5. Did this music make you want to DANCE or RELAX? _____
_____

Song #3:
1. Did you enjoy this music? _____
_____
2. Was this music FAST or SLOW? _____
_____
3. Was this song LOUD or QUIET? _____
_____
4. Did this music make you feel HAPPY or SAD? _____
_____
5. Did this music make you want to DANCE or RELAX? _____
_____

clear plastic or styrofoam cups
vinegar
cold water
plastic spoons
crayons
drying rack for eggs (can be made from empty
    egg cartons)

Procedure

1. Group assistants prepare the dye, following kit instructions.
2. Patients choose a dye color and gently place their eggs in the appropriate cup.
3. Patients monitor the egg color, being encouraged to turn or check eggs periodically.
4. When the egg color is satisfactory, the egg is removed from the dye and placed on the drying rack.
5. When dry, the eggs can be decorated with stickers and crayons.
6. A communal display of all the eggs can be photographed for later reference.
7. Eggs can be refrigerated, and later shelled, mashed, and mixed with mayonnaise for a simple egg salad served on bread.

Fourth of July Design

Materials
black construction paper
glitter (assorted colors)
white glue (small bottles)
tape

Procedure

Have an assistant distribute one piece of black construction paper to each member. Ask members to draw a fireworks design with glue. Next, have them sprinkle glitter onto glue areas and tap off the excess. When designs are dried, tape them together to make a large display.

Halloween Masks

Materials
writing and coloring implements
grocery bags

colored construction paper
tape
yarn
scissors

Procedure

Have members select a bag, cut out eye holes, and begin designing their masks in pencil. Next, encourage them to use markers to color in the features. Support creative, individualistic uses of construction paper to make ears, eyelashes, beards, mustaches, noses, etc.

Halloween Ghosts

Materials
cotton balls
facial tissues (white)
tape or yarn
black felt-tip marker

Procedure

Wrap tissues around cotton balls and fasten with tape or tie with yarn to secure. Draw eyes on ghosts with a felt-tip marker.

Thanksgiving: Turkey Centerpiece

Materials
copies of a turkey design
blunt scissors
crayons and markers for coloring
sugar-free lollipops
apples
tape

Procedure

Have members color and cut out turkey designs. Wrap the designs around lollipops and secure with tape. Poke the lollipops into apples and arrange in a circle for the centerpiece.

Christmas: Santa Faces

Materials

paper plates	red and white
cotton balls	construction paper
glue	tape
magic markers	blunt scissors

Procedure

Begin by having members cut a large triangle of red paper. Ask members to take four large paper plates and tape the red triangle on the upper half as a hat. Next, draw eyes, nose, and mouth on the plate and glue cotton around the edges of the hat and plate (as trim and a beard). Have members glue two pieces of cotton on to the tip of the hat as a tassle and cotton under the nose as a mustache. Finally, fill in cotton where needed to make a full, fluffy face.

9   Visual Memory Game

Therapeutic Rationale

This visual identification activity helps develop language skills and improve visual memory. Members are given the opportunity to support one another's efforts and applaud successes.

Materials

box
20 small objects (for example, paper clip, key, pencil, pen, rubber band, envelope, fork, photograph, coin, etc.)
blindfold or cardboard to cover entire box

Procedure

Discuss how memory skills can be developed through practice. Have a group assistant place ten of the objects in the box. Decide who will take the first turn. Let the first member study the objects carefully, while an assistant keeps time. Encourage the patient to pick up each item and describe it to the rest of the group. Then cover the box or blindfold the member. Count how many items the patient can correctly recall and describe. Go on to the next player.

10   Cellophane Windows

Therapeutic Rationale

This simple activity helps members understand the different stages of construction involved in producing a creative and artistic piece of work. The completed project, giving a stained glass effect, can be used to decorate and brighten patients' sleeping or recreational environment. This activity is designed to offer a sense of accomplishment and build confidence to participate in future group activities. By assisting in the discussion of the completed window designs, you and the other leaders foster communication skills. Mutual feedback skills will transfer to subsequent group meetings.

Materials

colored cellophane or tissue paper
construction paper
blunt scissors
glue stick, tape

Procedure

The patients select a color of construction paper. The paper is folded and members go on to cut shapes out of the paper. When cutting is finished, they choose assorted colors of tissue paper for the "windows." Elmer's Glue is used to adhere the tissue paper to the construction paper, creating the illusion of a stained glass window. If desired, the completed craft may be hung or placed on a window sill, or somewhere with ample light.

11   Seasonal Collage

Therapeutic Rationale

The task helps patients orient themselves to the present season. It also helps them to recall various things associated with that season—

holidays, foods, recreational pursuits, weather, flowers, etc. Patients are encouraged to express preferences and favorite seasonal activities. The project also builds manual dexterity and perceptual skills.

Materials

magazines   paper
crayons   tape or glue
blunt scissors   pencils

Procedure

Suggest to members that to get in the mood and prepare for a particular season it might be fun to make a collage with pictures and photographs representative of that season. Ask them to cut out pictures of things that remind them of the season and glue them onto a piece of paper. Invite members to draw pictures if they wish. Next to each picture, participants can write something to describe the picture, or write why that picture characterizes the season for them. The individual collages can be combined to form a giant group mural and hung in a public location.

Lower Functioning Patient Activities
1. select, cut and glue pictures
2. draw pictures or color others' picture
3. help hang collage

Higher Functioning Patient Activities
1. select, cut, and paste pictures
2. draw pictures and help others visualize their ideas
3. help others cut and paste
4. write comments alongside pictures

12   Graduation

Therapeutic Rationale

This activity is designed to highlight completion of the first structured group model, giving success feedback to members who have attended regularly. Granting a graduation certificate is concrete evidence of progress and publicly recognizes achievement. Individuals can show peers their certificates and communicate their pride. This process attracts others to the group and permits staff the opportunity to applaud the efforts made by the patients at increasing their therapeutic activities involvement.

Materials

certificates for graduation
ribbon (for tying rolled certificates prior to
    presentation ceremony)
cardboard
construction paper
tape
optional: refreshments (punch and cookies)
    and music (taped recordings)

The certificates can be designed by group leaders or former graduates. These should look as "official" as possible (see sample).

Procedure

At the meeting prior to the graduation ceremony, each member should be asked to invite one nongroup member to attend the graduation ceremony. (Sometimes just mentioning refreshments will serve to lure the nonmembers.) These nonmembers serve as an audience, and they can learn about the GIT program in the process.

The day of the ceremony have group assistants arrange chairs for the audience and graduating members. After everyone is seated in a somewhat formal manner, announce the purpose of the ceremony and review the GIT activities completed by members during this module. (Since this review should be brief, usually simply naming each meeting's activity is adequate. A poster listing the module's activities can be helpful.) Maintaining a formal tone, call each member by his or her full name to the front and present the certificate, saying something like, "In honor of your responsible group membership, we wish to present you with this token of your accomplishment." You can encourage clapping after each certificate is accepted. After all certificates have been presented, the group may break for light refreshments.

The members may want to make simple frames for their certificates using cardboard and construction paper. This activity can be pursued immediately, or can serve as an introductory task in the next GIT module, after the members have taken a week off for vacation.

Diploma

This is to certify that _____

has distinguished herself in the _____

_____ Group with outstanding performance

and an excellent attendance record.

On this day _____, _____, _____, 1985,

she became an honored member and advisor to the group. Her age is _____,

being born on _____, of _____.

She resides at _____.

Group Assistants:_____

_____

Task 12

Diploma

This is to certify that _____

has distinguished himself in the _____

_____ Group with outstanding performance

and an excellent attendance record.

On this day _____, _____, _____, 1985,

he became an honored member and advisor to the group. His age is _____,

being born on _____, of _____.

He resides at _____.

Group Assistants: _____

_____

GIT Module: Tasks 13–24

13   Introduction

Therapeutic Rationale
This activity allows for integration of new group members. While introducing them to the GIT approach, this session also gives former GIT members a chance to review and rehearse some of their acquired skills.

Materials
colored paper
scissors
markers and pens
tape
large piece of paper or blackboard and chalk

Procedure
Announce that the group is about to begin another module of activities. Explain that the purpose of this meeting is to introduce some new members to the GIT program and that veteran GIT members will be asked to participate as assistants.

    Ask for one volunteer to cut name tags out of the colored paper, a second volunteer to write out the first names of group members on the name tags, and a third to tape the name tags onto group members. Assemble the volunteer trio and have all other members line up for their name tags. Once everyone has a name tag, encourage the group to thank the volunteers. Explain to the new participants that in this group "the patients do most of the work and see to it that things work out right."

Next, ask members if they would be willing to try a memory game. See how many GIT activities they can remember from the previous module. List each remembered exercise on the large piece of paper or a blackboard. Then have members try to recall the best and worst features of each, for example, "The worst time when we were rooting those cuttings was when someone spilled perlite all over and we had to spend ten minutes cleaning up the mess . . . ; the best, how the big plant looked sitting in the sun!").

You and other leaders can freely share their memories of different activities. Telling group stories to new members makes the incoming participants feel a part of what has gone on before. Ask newcomers who might have watched the group as an observer if they remember seeing the group engage in any particular task that looked interesting. Encourage former members to explain what was going on during the observed meeting. This review process creates a sense of group history and shared achievement, which gets the newly formed group off to a good start.

14 Feelings Game

Therapeutic Rationale
This game fosters self-awareness. Patients are helped to get in touch with their feelings by learning many words for different feelings the participants might not have been able to differentiate. By providing a language for emotional expression, this experience encourages appropriate interpersonal communication and intimacy. It also helps members to understand how others feel and to learn how to express empathy. As a result, patients build closer relationships and communicate mutual concern and caring.

Materials
feelings identification sheet
construction paper
crayons

Use copies of the feelings identification sheet provided in this book or design your own (have group members write down different feelings and draw a face that represents that emotion). Any kind of paper can be used, but colored construction paper is appropriate because members can choose the color that best fits their emotions at the time. This in itself provides a helpful practice in labeling and expressing emotional states.

Procedure
Suggest to the patients that you have a game that might help them learn about their own and other people's feelings. Ask them to look at the words and faces on the feelings identification sheet and then circle the picture that best captures their mood. Members can then draw pictures of how they feel at that time. When they are done, have the group guess how each person feels that day by looking at what the individual drew. Members can then discuss whether that person's behavior and expression seem to match what they are feeling inside. Participants realize that others can't "read their minds" and that it's helpful to put inner experiences into words. Members can commiserate with one another about how hard it sometimes is to label and express feelings. The value of trying to do this can then be discussed.

Lower Functioning Patient Activities
1. Circle faces describing their emotions.

How Do You Feel Today?

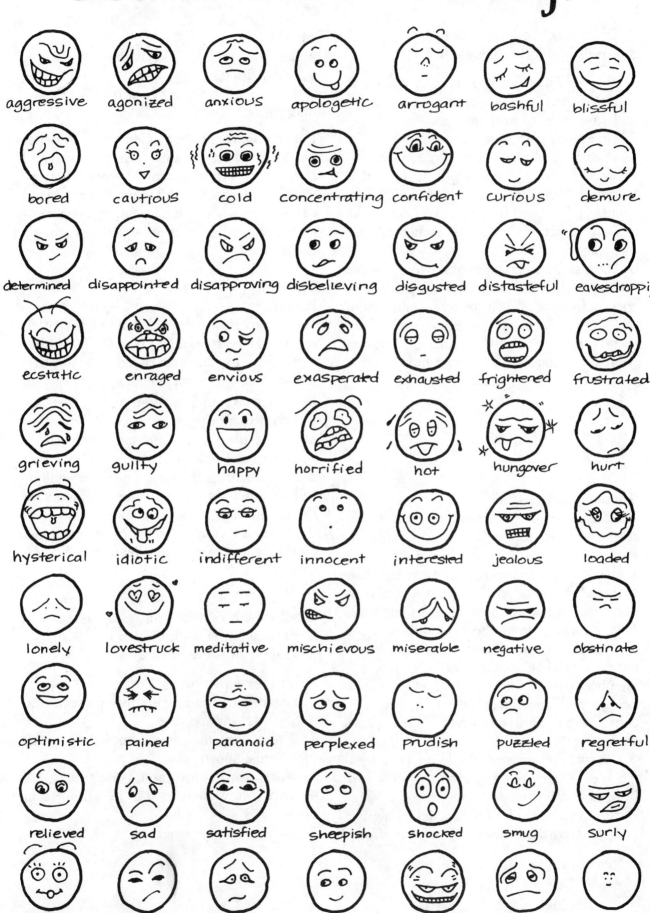

aggressive · agonized · anxious · apologetic · arrogant · bashful · blissful

bored · cautious · cold · concentrating · confident · curious · demure

determined · disappointed · disapproving · disbelieving · disgusted · distasteful · eavesdropping

ecstatic · enraged · envious · exasperated · exhausted · frightened · frustrated

grieving · guilty · happy · horrified · hot · hungover · hurt

hysterical · idiotic · indifferent · innocent · interested · jealous · loaded

lonely · lovestruck · meditative · mischievous · miserable · negative · obstinate

optimistic · pained · paranoid · perplexed · prudish · puzzled · regretful

relieved · sad · satisfied · sheepish · shocked · smug · surly

surprised · suspicious · sympathetic · thoughtful · turned-on · undecided · withdrawn

Task 14

2. Draw faces of how they feel.
3. Guess how other people feel.

Higher Functioning Patient Activities
1. Help others learn words they do not know.
2. Draw faces of how they feel.
3. Guess how other people feel.
4. Discuss the difficulties involved in expressing feelings, for example, "people use words to mean different things"; "feelings can change rapidly"; "it's hard to trust others and make oneself vulnerable"; "people sometimes act like they don't care" . . . etc.
5. Discuss the advantages of learning how to identify, label, and express feelings to close friends, for example, "helps others understand me"; "talking about problems can make them seem easier to handle"; "other people can sometimes suggest ideas about how to cope with problems" . . . etc.

15   Group Picture Book

Therapeutic Rationale

Making this communal book serves as a way for patients to develop fine motor skills using scissors or by drawing. The patients are also able to get in touch with what they like to do, what they would like to have, and who they really are by putting on paper things that interest them. After the book is finished, it can be used as a means of getting to know other patients and their interests. Individual members can do part of the task independently, and then later all participants can combine their efforts to produce one big collective book.

As some patients are discharged and new members enter the group, the old book can be used as a memory scrapbook and a "new edition" can be made. This creates a tangible archival record of shared cooperative effort.

Materials

paper	scissors
varied writing instruments	glue
magazines	yarn or a stapler

Use any kind of paper. (Construction paper works the best because it is stronger and comes in a variety of colors from which to choose.) Magazines with many different types of pictures work best. To put the pages together use either yarn or staples, whichever is preferred.

Procedure

Suggest to members that having a written record of the group might be nice. The group could use it to remember things done together and to show to new members. Begin by saying, "The book should be about us . . . what we like to do and things we enjoy." By cutting out magazine pictures and making drawings, the group can make its own special book that shows something about each member's unique self and interests. Each member will work on their own page, and use it to express something about their life. Then the group will join all the pages together and read the new creation.

Lower Functioning Patient Activities
1. select, cut out pictures, and paste
2. draw pictures with crayon or pencil
3. suggest possible themes

Higher Functioning Patient Activities
1. help other patients with drawings, cutting out, or writing names
2. discuss a theme for the book, for example, foods, sports, etc.
3. write a short story about themselves
4. discuss how pictures will be arranged in book
5. tie all pages together

16 Making Fruit Sherbert

Therapeutic Rationale

Making sherbert is a way to boost patient group involvement, because food is a primary reinforcer. Sherbert is especially appealing on a hot summer day. The patients can discuss their likes and dislikes in choosing a flavor. Each individual can add one ingredient, and with group cooperation can create a treat to which each individual contributed. When members are done preparing the sherbert, they can enjoy eating their creation.

Materials

blender   ice
frozen juice   cups
  concentrate   spoons

(Any flavor juice can be used, depending on people's likes and dislikes.)

Procedure

Suggest to members that they could prepare something to eat by combining their efforts. They could all cooperate to make one thing together, which they all will enjoy eating afterwards. Ask the group for flavor suggestions and help them reach a decision. Assistance with compromising, for example, "We'll start with the most popular choice today, and try other flavors next time . . . ," helps teach negotiating skills.

Lower Functioning Patient Activities
1. discuss flavors enjoyed
2. measure ice and juice concentrate and put in blender
3. assist in cleanup

Higher Functioning Patient Activities
1. discuss flavors desired
2. read simple recipe
3. help other patients measure ice and juice
4. mix ingredients in blender
5. serve sherbert

17 Miniature Golf

Therapeutic Rationale

This golfing activity develops fine and gross motor skills and provides experience with an adult recreational activity. Participation rekindles memories of golfing experiences prior to hospitalization and fosters a sense of relationship with the outside community. It lets members identify with the golf professionals they watch on television. It also increases the vicarious satisfaction associated with this particular sport.

Materials

golf clubs (at least one putter for every five
    clients is best)
golf balls (plastic versions are available and
    can be useful with patients who might
    throw and abuse regular balls)
two large pieces of cardboard
scissors
paper
drawing implements
tape or glue

Procedure

Members can first be asked if they have ever played golf or miniature golf before. Those that respond affirmatively can be encouraged to briefly describe their experiences. Next, ask members if they would like to try creating a miniature golf hole to use. Explain that there will be different steps involved and that everyone will be able to join in the project. Tell them that later each member will have a turn to play.

The group must choose a theme for their golf hole. If members do not generate any ideas, you can make some suggestions, for example, outer space, race cars, farm animals, the ocean or beach, the city, another country, etc. A patient assistant can make a list of possible themes and lead the group in voting.

Some participants can draw and color pictures reflecting the selected theme, which can then be cut out and affixed to one piece of cardboard out of which a four-inch hole has been cut. A paper "ramp" can be fashioned onto this "green." Finally, a tee can be created on the remaining piece of cardboard by making a few indentations. (See sample diagram.) After this preparatory work is done, members can line up and begin to play.

Lower Functioning Patient Activities
1. vote on favorite theme

2. draw and/or color theme designs
3. glue or tape on designs
4. practice putting

Higher Functioning Patient Activities
1. select theme—list ideas and conduct voting
2. design hole's layout and suggest picture
3. tape on "ramps"
4. cut 4" hole and make tee indentation
5. practice putting
6. keep scores for players

Task 17

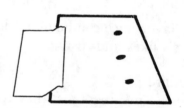

18 Making Statues

Therapeutic Rationale
This "sculpting" task produces an impressive, artistic outcome which typically draws compliments from other patients and staff members. Members make choices about statue content, color and design, and help assemble the communal product.

Materials
metal hangers (to make stands supporting

statues) or large piece of heavy cardboard for backing
newspaper
masking tape
colored construction paper
old tee shirts and old clothes
food color
poster paints and brush

Procedure
Members decide what kinds of statues they would like to create. You can offer suggestions, such as those included in the following list.

Cardboard
Backing

Hanger Stand

Relief Statues

Task 18

• current group members (have members choose their favorite color; cut paper hair to match their hairstyle)
  • Statue of Liberty for Independence Day celebration (use light green)
  • a golf pro (for the winner of miniature golf tournament)

Once the group has selected their subject, have members crumble newspaper and then tape balls of newspaper together to create the basic statue form. Participants can help cover the form with masking tape. Next, the form can be painted. Once the paint has dried, hair and details can be taped onto the figure. Finally, cloth can be draped onto the figure (a few drops of food coloring can be used to dye old tee shirts the desired colors ahead of time) and secured with tape for the figure's garment. (See sample figures.)

Lower Functioning Patient Activities
1. vote on statue subject
2. pick color(s) for statue(s)
3. crumple newspapers
4. add masking tape
5. paint figure
6. dye tee shirts

Higher Functioning Patient Activities
1. suggest statue subject
2. sketch statue ideas
3. arrange newspaper balls on cardboard or frame made from a hanger
4. design, cut, and tape on details
5. drape cloth to simulate garment

19 Leader Commemoration

Therapeutic Rationale
This activity gives patients an opportunity to express their appreciation to departing group leaders. Members prepare small commemorative items which reflect personal interests and tastes, and give them as presents to leaders.

Recognizing leaders in this way helps equalize the patient-staff relationship and therefore fosters members' self-esteem. Members also learn how to cope with the difficult termination process.

Materials
paper, tape
writing and drawing implements; typewriter (depends on types of presents members choose to make)
magazines for cutting out collage pictures
cardboard to make a picture frame
empty cans and yarn to make pencil holders or vases
colored tissue paper to make paper flowers
optional: simple refreshments

Procedure
In advance of the "going-away" meeting, you can suggest to members that it would be nice to celebrate the other leader's departure with a present. The group can discuss possible mementos that could be made out of available materials. You can make suggestions, if necessary (for example, write and frame a group poem; make a stack of handmade thank you cards; prepare a pencil holder or vase by wrapping yarn around an empty can; make paper flowers in a vase; make a big magazine photo collage card; etc.). Members can work on different presents in small subgroups. Participants can be encouraged to express their own memories and feelings about the leader.

At the departing leader's last group meeting, items can be presented individually. This leader can thank each member and give reassurance that he or she will not be forgotten.

If desired, simple refreshments, for example, cookies and coffee, can be shared afterwards.

Lower Functioning Patient Activities
• draw and color designs for thank you cards

• wrap yarn around cans to make pencil holders or vases

- make simple paper flowers (see diagram that follows this task)

Higher Functioning Patient Activities
- write a poem, type or print it neatly, frame it

- design paper flower bouquet
- create thank you cards for other members to color

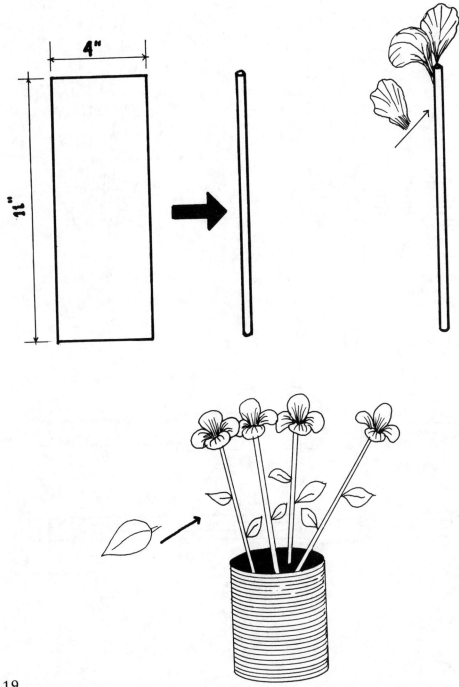

Task 19

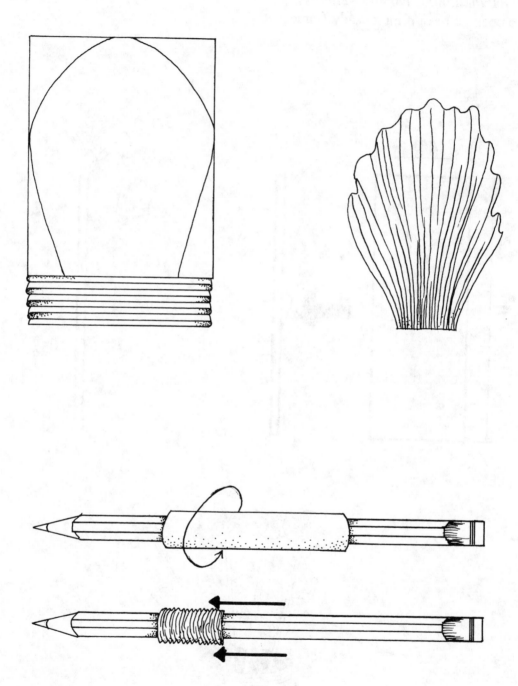

Task 19

20 Growing Flowers From Seed

Therapeutic Rationale

Most GIT patients have considerable interest in gardening. Nurturing plants provides tangible evidence of the patients' ability to control outcomes. This task promotes use of fine motor skills in the actual planting procedure. Decisions must be made by a patient concerning the appropriate amount of soil to use in the flat, the type of flower seeds to plant, and how much water to use after planting.

The follow-up task is designed to encourage an interest in the outcome and care of the plants by setting up a water and checkup schedule. Each patient has a day to perform a check on the plants, fostering task ownership and a sense of responsibility. Hopefully, it will also enable patients to feel gratified and expectant about a pending event that they were instrumental in bringing about. The communal effort reinforces the value of cooperation, builds group identity, and provides members with a basis for future conversations.

Materials

plastic flats for starting seeds
potting and starter soil
seeds: marigold, zinnia, lima, and green beans
styrofoam cups (for soil and water)

Procedure

After explaining the project to the patients, the flats are distributed. A pail or bag of soil is available on the table and the patients can take as much as they need. The group is advised about the amount of soil to put in each section of the flat so that there will be room for the seeds and a topcoat of soil. Patients then choose which type of seed they want to plant and are given advice on amount of seeds used for each section. Soil is then added to cover the seeds and the flats are watered. The final task is to ask for volunteers to follow a daily plant-check schedule. The schedule is then posted near the flats for reference.

Lower Functioning Modification

Plant misters can be made from discarded nonaerosol bottles, for example, hairspray, cleanser bottles, etc. After carefully cleaning bottles, they can be decorated and individualized. Using the misters for watering allows more patients to assume responsibility for the watering and also prevents excessive plant hydration.

21 Taste Memory Game

Therapeutic Rationale

This identification game helps patients explore how the senses work and gives practice in using senses to identify and match foods. Mutual encouragement among members helps to pull feelings of trust and companionship.

Materials

different tasting foods (for example, bananas, pickles, ham, lettuce, cookies, cheese, oranges, spices in jars)
blindfold

Procedure

Explain that the object of this game is to identify food samples by taste, smell, and texture. Have members decide how to take turns in this identification. After blindfolding, have a player examine the first sample food carefully; encourage the participant to smell and feel how the food is shaped. See if the player can identify the food item. Go on to the next player.

22 Modified Aerobic Dancing

Therapeutic Rationale

This activity combines music and movement in an effort to interest members in a form of exercise requiring only modest physical exertion and stamina. Many patients on major tranquilizers must struggle to maintain a healthful weight, because these drugs frequently sap energy and reduce physical activity. Weight gain is a common result. This group activity makes exercise seem more appealing and gradually increases members' flexibility and stamina.

Materials

tape recorder
cassette tape with recordings of several slow
   rhythmic selections

Procedure

A group assistant can arrange chairs in a large circle. Gather members together and discuss the health benefits of regular, nonstrenuous exercise. You should mention that it is unwise to embark on a very ambitious athletic routine all at once, that it's necessary to get into better physical shape gradually in order to avoid possible injury. You might also mention that exercising together in a group can be a way of maintaining interest and enthusiasm.

Tell the group that each member will be taking a turn at suggesting a movement to accompany the music. All members will perform that action until the leader lets them know it's time to move on to a new movement. Start with having the patients in a seated position. A group assistant can start the tape, while you perform a simple and slow movement designed to help members warm up their muscles. Gradually bending the neck forward and from side to side is a good movement to use initially. Continue for about one minute.

A second movement involves extending the arms forward and then moving them back in time to the music for about one minute, allowing all members time to learn how to imitate. The third movement could be making small circles with the arms extended from the sides. Then have each member take a turn suggesting a simple movement that can be performed while sitting. Depending on the group's level of fitness, you may decide to conclude this activity with additional movements from the seated position, or move on to movements done while standing. As the group's ability increases, faster musical selections and more rigorous routines can be attempted.

23 Making Calendars

Therapeutic Rationale

This group activity fosters temporal orientation throughout the year by providing individualized calendars for all group members. It permits members to remember and plan for "special days," which helps build a sense of community and continuity. Patients congratulate one another on birthdays, contributing to a sense of concern and belongingness. A personal calendar becomes invaluable as patients progress and become more involved in various activities. This tool helps them organize their time and schedule therapy and work tasks. Our method of creating calendars offers the opportunity for those with artistic talent to create satisfying masterpieces. Those members with more modest abilities also experience success and satisfaction. Making calendars is an especially appropriate way to celebrate the new year, following a discussion about New Year's resolutions and hopes for growth and change.

Materials

calendar grid pages (make 6 copies per patient) (see sample diagram)

varied writing, coloring, painting implements

assortment of stickers

sample calendars (at least one should have large, highly legible numbers)

stapler

magazine photos, tissue paper, or hand drawings for collage cover

clear acetate or clear plastic adhesive paper (for example, contact paper)

tape

glue stick

optional—large calendar:

> sheet of colored tag or heavy bond (roughly 18″ × 24″)
>
> piece of cardboard (roughly 18″ × 24″)
>
> tape, scissors, marker, 8″ × 11½″ paper
>
> heavy duct tape

Procedure

Have a group assistant distribute calendar pages to members, counting out six per patient, or have each member count out their own six pages. You can demonstrate how to fold pages to assemble the calendar. Patients can then staple pages together and put their name on the back of the calendar.

Pass out sample calendars and help members label the months on their calendar. For some patients, it is helpful to indicate the first and last date on each month, in order to prevent undue frustration and copying errors. Let members choose a pen, crayon, or marker to fill in the numbers on their calendar.

Patients who are quick to complete the numbering process can begin to design their calendar cover, using various art materials.

Once all members are finished numbering their months, have everyone discuss which "special days" should be marked. Members' birthdays and holidays can be designated with stickers or handwritten designs. The group may even decide to mark its "GIT anniversary date"—a special holiday shared only by GIT members and graduates.

Lower Functioning Patient Activities

Since numbering all twelve months can be tedious for patients with graphic dysfunctions, with lower functioning patients a leader may choose to prenumber all or most months in advance of copying pages. The member will need a role model to help in learning how to sequence the months correctly.

A simple way to create an attractive calendar cover is to invite members to cut out photos they like or random shapes from brightly colored tissue paper. These can be glued to the front and then protected with a cover of acetate or clear adhesive paper.

Higher Functioning Patient Activities

These patients can assist less able participants with the assembling and numbering process.

It is also a good idea to have high-level patients begin preliminary work on a large group calendar (if one isn't already available in the treatment room).

Communal Calendar

A reusable group calendar can be made by taking a colored piece of oak tag and cutting out holes in a 6″ by 7″ grid pattern. A hole for the month's name could also be cut (see illustration).

After this challenging step is finished, the piece of tag can be taped to a cardboard backing (of comparable size) on three sides, but not the top.

Five pieces of regular paper can be taped together to create a large insert, placed between the tag and cardboard levels.

A patient can write in the month and fill in the days at the beginning of each new month. Group plans should be penciled in on this communal calendar.

At the end of each month, a group assistant can remove the old paper insert, which can be stored for later reference, and create its replacement. The calendar can be attached to the wall with heavy duct tape.

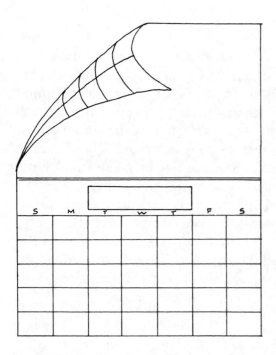

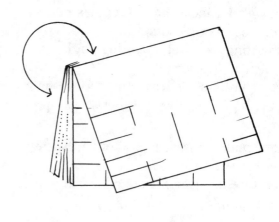

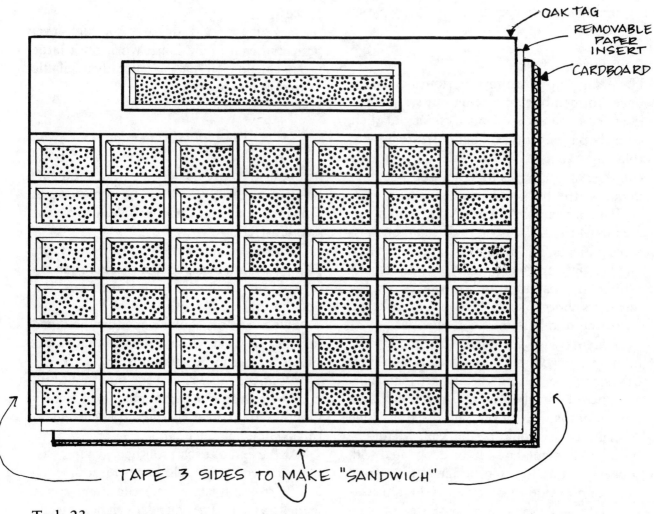

TAPE 3 SIDES TO MAKE "SANDWICH"

Task 23

Task 23

S	M	T	W	T	F	S

24 Graduation

Therapeutic Rationale
This graduation tradition provides both members and leaders with a sense of completion and closure. It affords formal recognition of the group members' shared accomplishments.

Materials and Procedure
Same as GIT Task 12, except former graduates who remember the procedure may be asked to take a more active role in organizing the graduation room and ceremony.

GIT Module III: Tasks 25–36

---

25 Introductions

Therapeutic Rationale
Same as GIT Task 13, except former members who remember the procedure can be given a greater role in organizing the meeting.

26 Individual GIT Journals

Therapeutic Rationale
Keeping a personal individual journal after each GIT meeting can assist members in consolidating their learning experiences. Trying to list the names of attending members provides motivation to learn and recall peers' names. Rating one's own task success and enjoyment forces patients to reflect on personal experiences, form opinions, and make decisions about how to express views. Indicating future plans helps patients recognize the need to formulate objectives in advance, and helps them feel involved in the planning process. At the end of a module, a completed journal gives a sense of accomplishment and completion.

Materials
journal sheets (see sample)
stapler
paper (for covers)
writing and coloring implements

Procedure
Ask group members if they have ever kept a diary or a journal. You can suggest the possibility that keeping a record of group activities might make their GIT experiences more meaningful to them. Have an assistant distribute pages, enough for ten meetings, to each member, along with a blank sheet for a journal cover. Members can assemble and staple their journals, then decorate them according to individual preferences. At the end of each meeting, their journals can be distributed. With your assistance, when necessary, members can be encouraged to complete as much of the journal page as they can. Journals can be collected and distributed at the end of the next meeting.

Higher Functioning Modification
More capable members can be encouraged to keep their journals with other belongings.

27 Playing the Ungame

Therapeutic Rationale
This activity develops communication skills, as patients listen to one another and respond to the various questions generated. Expressiveness and openness are reinforced, allowing greater intimacy and growth among members. Questions can be arranged in order to facilitate progressively increasing self-disclosure. Cooperation is fostered by team play and

My GIT Journal

Day _____

Names (who came to group today)

_____

_____

_____

_____

_____

_____

What did we do? _____

_____

_____

Today's activity or project: _____

_____

_____

What did I learn? _____

_____

_____

What skills were practiced or developed? _____

_____

_____

Rating my success at the task: yes   no _____

Rating of my enjoyment: yes   no _____

Future (plans for next meeting): _____

_____

_____

Task 26

In honor of...

_____

Advance 5 Spaces!

shared progress on the team board. The game provides a forum for sharing all kinds of information (about self, hospital procedures, coping techniques, etc.). Repeated playings allow members to select many different content areas for emphasis.

Materials

For each game set:
- large piece of cardboard (possibly cut from discarded supermarket carton)
- 30 3″ × 5″ pieces of paper or index cards
- 30 8½″ × 11″ bond, cut in half (widthwise) or large index cards to make game cards
- tape
- marker
- crayons, paints, or markers for coloring board
- small objects or figures to serve as playing pieces (the group can make and reuse these pieces)

Procedure

Two meetings are usually required for the ungame: one for setting up and at least one for play. Members can prepare a game board by coloring 3″ by 5″ rectangles and then taping them to create a curved path (see diagram following this task). Playing pieces can be found or made from any available materials. Next, players are asked to create several ungame questions, after a few examples are read by the leader. A group assistant can write the simplified questions in large block letters on the game cards.

Members can be divided into teams if the group is large. Each team is asked to decide on a playing piece. Each team takes a turn selecting a card and responding to its question. After all of one team's members have given their answers, feedback is asked of the other players. As the leader, you can model applause for a good effort (usually all other players will follow suit and clap enthusiastically after each team play). A team participant advances the team playing piece on the board.

The first team to complete play can be commemorated with a special game card reading, "In honor of team members (blank spaces for patients to write their names), advance 5 spaces." This card is then added to the deck. It allows former winners to be remembered positively each time this card is drawn by a lucky team.

Game card questions can be varied endlessly, depending on group members' abilities and inventiveness. Concrete and factual questions can be used with lower ability patients; more abstract questions ("What is the best age to be?") can challenge higher functioning members. It is useful to include questions that address coping strategies—"What can you do when you wake up in a bad mood?" or "What can you do when someone has an angry outburst?" Peer support and advice is welcomed when players are trying to respond to difficult questions.

28   Basic Food Groups

Therapeutic Rationale

Since eating is universal, tasks that involve food provide a guaranteed common ground for discussion. Patients tend to be quite interested in thinking about foods; even resistant group members respond to inquiries about their eating preferences. Since hospitalized patients typically eat communally, leaders' questions about recent meals foster a bond among those who speak from shared experience. Even a critical discourse on the inadequacies of institutional cuisine can provide an interesting departure point for this group task. After voicing opinions about their meals, patients can be challenged to think about the reasons underlying the hospital's menu choices.

The activity develops both communication and decision-making skills. The experience gives practice in assertive self-expression, and lets members observe role models accepting and applauding individual differences, thereby fostering tolerance of others. Patients learn the rudiments of balanced nutrition, which can be applied when eating in less structured and supervised settings. Members also gain some insight into the rationale behind the hospital's food selections, often enhancing appreciation for the dietary department.

Materials

newsprint and markers
posterboard

old magazines
blunt scissors
paste

Procedure

To begin, ask patients if they like to eat (most respond affirmatively). Next, go around the table and ask each member (leaders included, of course) to tell the group his or her most and least favorite food. You or a patient assistant can make two large newsprint lists of all responses. Any overlapping or contradictory responses (when one person's least favorite food is another's most favorite) can be noted. Commonalities can foster member identification, differences can be appreciated as interesting and potentially useful (for example, "Well, if we ever have liver, since you hate it, you could share yours with him!").

Patients are asked how they feel about hospital food. Usually negative comments burst forth, although some patients may defend particular items. (If undergraduate co-leaders are helping to run the group, parallels between their campus menus and the hospital's are interesting to make, and help to "normalize" the patients' eating experience, for example, "I guess we all have seen too much chicken tettrazini!")

After this discussion, you or another leader can raise questions about why patient menus are the way they are—who decides what patients eat and what factors guide that decision-making process. This can lead to talk about the cost of various foods, the almost universal need to budget, and the difficulty of preparing different foods. Patients can be asked about their own cooking experiences (this can help assess which members could serve as patient assistants during a later GIT cookbook task). The conversation can finally be directed toward the issue of basic food groups and the need for a nutritionally balanced diet. A brief explanation of the four basic food groups usually suffices.

Basic Nutrition Information

Concept: Food composition for proper basic nutrition

Key Words: Calorie, protein, carbohydrate, fat, fiber

What should a good diet do for your?

— A good diet should be nutritionally sound and supply basic nutrients to support daily activity and maintain body stores for periods of stress.

— It should provide for an even distribution of food throughout the day to give relief from hunger pains and maintain an even energy level.

— If you are attempting to reduce your weight, it should reduce the number of calories taken in below the caloric expenditure. This forces the body to burn stored fat to meet your energy requirements.

Definitions

Calorie: A calorie is a unit for measuring the heat or energy producing capacity of food when it is burned by the body. Food adds calories; activity burns them, including sleeping or breathing. When "calories in" equals "calories out," weight is maintained.

Protein: A protein is the basic material of each body cell, required for growth and maintenance. Proteins are composed of amino acids, of which nine are essential. Animal proteins are of higher quality than vegetable, but the two may be combined for good nutrition. Good protein is found in eggs, milk, cheese, fish, meats, poultry, soy beans, beans and peas, grains, cereals, and nuts.

Carbohydrate: A carbohydrate is used as the source for body activity or heat, basically sugars or starches. Excess carbohydrate is converted into fat. Sources: breads, cereal products, rice, noodles, most vegetables, fruits, sugar, jellies, candy, and honey.

Fats: Fats are another source of energy, doubly as rich as proteins and carbohydrates. They delay stomach emptying time and thus make food seem more satisfying. Some essential unsaturated fatty acids are essential for good nutrition and are found in vegetable oils. Other sources: fatty meats, dairy products, oils, and nuts.

Minerals: Minerals are inorganic substances vital to body function, found in hard tissue, bones, and teeth. Calcium is found in milk, cheese, shellfish, egg yolk, soy beans, and broccoli. Iron can be found in liver, shellfish, egg yolk, dried beans and fruits, cereals. Iodine can be found in seafoods and iodized salt.

Vitamins: Vitamins are necessary for proper utilization of food and for healthy body functioning. A varied diet is the best way to obtain them all.

Fiber: Indigestible component of most plant foods, made up largely of cellulose. Fiber in diet helps regular elimination.

Explain the importance of a balanced diet and suggest that members try to include foods from the four basic food groups in each day's meals:
1. meats and eggs
2. dairy products
3. fruits and vegetables
4. grains and cereals

Next, the group can be asked to give examples of foods from each of the four food groups discussed earlier. An engaging and interesting vehicle for this activity is to make a collage. Photographs of these foods can be torn from magazines and pasted onto a large poster board divided into four sections. Artistic members can draw and color their food examples. If a menu for the next hospital meal is available, patients can check it to see if all food groups are being appropriately represented.

29 Yarn Mascots

Therapeutic Rationale
This task helps members develop creativity and get practice in expressing feelings and emotions. These yarn mascots are cute and fun to make. At the end of the project, members can make up a story about their furry friends. The mascots can be displayed in the patients' rooms. Every time the members see the mascots, they will take pleasure in knowing they produced something of their own. Members may elect to give their mascots to someone else as a friendship gift.

Materials

yarn	felt
glue	tongue depressors
scissors	or popsicle sticks
little plastic eyes	cardboard

Procedure
Yarn color is chosen by the members. Each patient then wraps the yarn around his hand until the yarn is 2″ thick by 4″ wide. A 9″ piece is tied around the middle of the ball. Scissors are used to cut through the yarn "loops," disconnecting them. The yarn is fluffed and trimmed to desired shape. Plastic eyes (with glue on the back) are placed on fuzzies, along with red felt for a mouth and a different colored felt piece for a nose. Feet are then attached (tongue depressors or popsicle sticks, cardboard or felt can be used).

30 Treasure Hunt

Therapeutic Rationale

This recreational pursuit provides members with valuable practice in following directions and labels and with maps. It also helps develop planning and organizational skills. Patients gain experience in simple problem solving and learn how to anticipate others' reactions.

Materials

large maps of area (exterior or interior, depending on weather)
large pieces of tracing paper
crayons or soft pencils (for tracing course)
felt-tip markers, pens or pencils
paper
scissors
"treasures" (a jar of decaffeinated coffee or tea, a colorful flag, a bright poster (any desirable item can work)
"runners-up" prizes (any token of participation)

Procedure

In advance of the actual hunt, members divide into two subgroups—each to develop a treasure-hunt course for members of the other subgroup. When the weather is warm, participants might be encouraged to chart an outdoor course, which can help patients become more familiar with the surrounding area. An indoor course can help acquaint patients with special offices or therapeutic rooms. Both subgroups can use a large exterior or interior map for planning their courses.

The subgroups can discuss where they could hide the treasure and clues. Members can mark each depot on their map and chart the overall course. They can take turns tracing the course by placing a piece of tracing paper over the large map and using crayon or soft pencil. This procedure generates a copy for each member of the other subgroup to consult during the actual hunt. Clues can be written on paper cut into rectangles. Destinations should be clearly labeled on all maps (all leaders may need to help at this stage).

On the day of the hunt, members work together to hide clues and the treasure. To begin the treasure hunt, have patients from each of the two subgroups pair up and exchange maps. Runners-up prizes can be distributed to all but the winning participants (ribbons, certificates, snack items, etc. all make suitable tokens of involvement).

31 Popular Song Recording

Therapeutic Rationale

This task is designed to foster group solidarity, social anxiety. Patients get practice in overcoming inhibitions, and delight in producing a communal musical project. Feelings of importance and confidence are increased. Members learn how to detect and correct errors, and are rewarded for this attention to detail by an impressive final product.

Materials

requires a tape recorder
a blank cassette tape
large typed lyric sheets
taped recordings of a few popular songs
supplementary materials: rhythm instruments (bought or group-made)

Procedure

Prior to the meeting, have members suggest names of songs they enjoy listening to and singing along with. Using this list, prepare a cassette tape recording and lyric sheets in advance of the "song festival." Patients may help leaders write or type up the lyric sheets (try to use popular, main verses of songs).

Have group assistants distribute the lyric sheets. An assistant can be taught how to operate the cassette recorder. Run through each song a few times, having members sing along with the taped version until they are able to follow the lyrics reasonably well. You and the other leaders work individually with patients who have limited reading skills.

After the practice period is over, take the blank cassette and record the group singing each song. If there are problems with the lyrics of melodies during the first taping, teach members how to rewind the tape and then make a better version. This provides patients with leader-mediated experiences with detecting errors, giving and receiving constructive feedback, and correcting mistakes. Persistence is rewarded by a higher quality final product. Members can work until they are satisfied with how their tape sounds, and then sit back and listen to or sing along with their own musical creation.

32 Making Greeting Cards

Therapeutic Rationale
The same general method described under GIT invitations can be used to make inexpensive all-occasion greeting cards. In past GIT groups cards have been made for all holidays and seasons, and for get well, birthday, thank you, and congratulatory purposes. Patients can share these cards with other GIT members, friends, relatives, and (most importantly) staff members whom they wish to remember on various occasions.

Members can initiate pen pals, stay in touch with former GIT members, or send cards to a targeted group they're concerned about, for example, ailing children, AIDS patients, etc. These cards provide a ready mechanism for communicating concern for others, and often yield a hefty return of caring and concern.

Sending cards to disadvantaged or victimized groups reduces self-absorption and allows patients to use personal comparison as a means of coping with and overcoming self-pity. This activity gives members a chance to act on their vague fears and concerns (often engendered by the media), resulting in an enhanced sense of control and efficacy. Over the years we have tried, and generally been impressed with the results of, the following applications:

Types of Cards

Holiday
Seasonal
Get Well
Birthday
Thank You (widely varied content)
Congratulations
New Baby
Thinking of You . . .
Sorry I Missed . . .
I Wish We Could . . .
It's OK that you . . .
Let's Be Friends
You Make Me Laugh

Group-Selected Recipients

Friends
Relatives
Staff
Workshop Supervisors
Hospital Administrators
Politicians
God
Media Personalities
Blood Donors
Pen Pals:
 Scout Troops
 Church Groups
 Nursing Home Residents
 Police/Firemen

Empathy/Altruism Project Choices
Hospitalized Children
AIDS Patients

Soldiers (Veterans)
Earthquake, Fire, Mudslide Victims
Other Mental Health Clients
Unadopted Children

Materials
(See GIT Invitation Task 1.)

Procedure
Lower Functioning Patient Activities
• Before holidays, ask patients if they want to send greetings to anyone.
• When staff members are sick or leave, ask members if they'd like to send cards.
• Explore patients' empathy level ("Do you ever feel sorry for other people?" "Who do you sometimes feel sorry for?").
• Consider possible altruistic responses ("How could we help them feel better?")
• Have patients prepare cards.
• Ask patients to imagine recipients' responses to cards ("I bet they really felt good to know we cared!").

Higher Functioning Patient Activities
• With members, talk about assertiveness and self-expression.
• Discuss with participants the difficulty in saying important things in person.
• Explore members' unexpressed feelings and thoughts ("Is there anything you really wish you could say to someone you care about?").
• Ask patients to consider means of expressing ideas and ways of phrasing sentiments.
• Talk with members about the possible consequences of self-expression.
• Have participants make decisions about communications.
• Initiate a general discussion about caring ("Why does it feel good to know someone is thinking about us?" "Why does it feel good to let someone know you wish them well?").
• Discuss groups of people that the patients sometimes worry about ("Who could benefit from our concern?" "Who could we help to

feel better?" "Who would you like to help?").
• Have members consider how some disadvantaged and victimized groups handle their difficulties ("How do they cope?" "What can we learn from them?").
• Have the group prepare a care package to some designated needy group.

33 Clay Designs

Therapeutic Rationale
Clay molding lets patients work with their hands. Manipulating this material is sensual; many find it intrinsically reinforcing. Members get satisfaction from creating something for themselves that is both tangible and permanent.

The clay preparation requires cooperation and following simple directions. When the clay is dry, patients can use their imagination in painting their unique designs.

Materials

flour	spoon
salt	paints
water	paint brushes
large bowl	

Recipe: use 2 cups flour, ½ cup salt, ½ cup water to make 2 cups of clay. Mix in bowl.

Procedure
Introduce members to the idea of sculpting by bringing in books about pottery or sculpture. Suggest that the group might make and mold clay. Encourage members to plan what they will try to make with their clay, explaining that there's no right or wrong. Suggest things that they might try: bowls, ashtrays, or vases. Ask assistants to help add and mix ingredients. Members can take turns kneading the clay. Distribute the clay among patients and have them knead and mold it. Later, after the clay dries, have members paint their crea-

tions and arrange a small art display for other patients to see.

Lower Functioning Patient Activities
1. measure and add ingredients
2. mix ingredients
3. mold clay
4. paint the clay

Higher Functioning Patient Activities
1. help others measure and add ingredients
2. organize display of members' works; label individual projects

34 Auditory Memory Game

Therapeutic Rationale
This sound identification activity refines auditory perception and memory of different sounds. Patients offer mutual support and practice giving and receiving compliments.

Materials
objects that create a variety of sounds—bell, whistle, toy horn, kleenex box, alarm clock, keys, salt shaker, etc.

Procedure
Distribute items to members. Go around the group, having members demonstrate their object's sound. A few repetitions may be helpful. After all members say that they think they can remember each object's sound, collect all the materials. Have the participants cover their eyes while a leader sounds each object at random. Keep track of a member's success at identifying sounds.

35 Puppet Show

Therapeutic Rationale
Puppet shows give members the chance to be creative and to entertain others. Members are rewarded for expressing their ideas during the script-writing phase, and develop greater confidence in their talent as story tellers. Developing scenery and single puppet characters expands visual motor skills and emphasizes the value of cooperation. Reading skills are practiced during rehearsals. The activity also helps desensitize members to public situations and to speaking in front of others.

Materials
assorted paper, yarn, markers, paint, sticks, cardboard (from discarded boxes)
large table (turned on its sides and used as a theatre)
optional: popcorn, hot air popcorn maker, styrofoam cups, tape recorder and blank cassette tape, additional props (for example, a bag of fallen leaves for throwing during a fall scene, white confetti to represent snow, etc.)

Procedure
The group first must generate a topic for the puppet show. Writing a script about the experiences of two children during a particular season of the year is a way of maximizing potential member involvement, since all members were children at one time and all have had firsthand experience of different seasons.

The group can suggest alternatives and work on names and ages for the main characters. With your help, members can decide what these main characters look like (hair, dress, eye color, etc.).

Next, have patients sit back and recall their memories of particular times of the year. Ask them what they most like and dislike about a certain season. Have the group select about five concepts for the script. For each of these concepts, make a cardboard scene and any supplementary figures or props. The group can also work collectively to design the main cardboard characters, which can be attached to long sticks with tape, for maneuverability.

A more highly verbal group member can help write out a simple script with your assistance. Try to allow for sound effects or humorous props, for example, throwing confetti or leaves. Incorporate some simple group comments for members who won't have major roles. Make typed copies of the final script.

Members can divide the part they'd most like to play. After roles are assigned, have the participants practice their lines. Group lines can be practiced by all members, especially those who can't read more complex words. Then prepare a tape recording of the play. This allows for correcting errors. Encourage all members to participate in making funny sound effects.

Members can invite other patients to watch. Popcorn can be given as an enticement. Have two group assistants move characters as the tape plays.

36   Graduation

Therapeutic Rationale
This graduation tradition provides both members and leaders with a sense of completion and closure. It affords formal recognition of the group members' shared accomplishments.

Materials and Procedure
Same as GIT Task 12, except former graduates who remember the procedure may be asked to take a more active role in organizing the graduation room and ceremony.

GIT Module IV: Tasks 37–48

---

37   Introductions

Therapeutic Rationale
The meeting is designed to acquaint members with the more advanced GIT module objectives. The activities are intended for more advanced patients, who often need to develop skills relevant to community placement. The basic social interaction skills and life skills covered in modules IV and V are also applicable to patients likely to remain hospitalized a bit longer. Membership in a more advanced GIT group signifies to patients their successful completion of the introductory training. This task attempts to build the advanced group's special identity in the minds of members, and to foster peer support and mutual recognition.

Materials
marker
newsprint or large piece of paper
tape for mounting paper to wall

Procedure
Welcome members to their new advanced GIT experience. The meeting can be opened with an "ice breaker,"—each member can introduce the person sitting to his or her left. A sign-in sheet (to record group attendance) can be passed around. Later, an assistant can be made responsible for keeping the attendance book and remembering to bring and circulate it at meetings.

Spend a few minutes discussing the general objectives of the advanced GIT group, emphasizing that the participants have earned membership by successfully participating in earlier parts of the GIT program. Anecdotes about each member's group triumphs can be shared if any of the leaders have had prior experience with particular patients. After explaining that this advanced group will learn and share information about various living skills, you may want to give the participants the chance to decide on a name for their newly constituted GIT group. Suggested group names can be listed on a large sheet of paper, and a vote taken. Any attempts to combine names to create a workable compromise can be supported by the leaders.

Next, the group can review a list of ten possible topics for consideration (GIT Tasks from Module IV). You can ask members to select five activities to cover. Inform participants that after these activities are completed each member will receive a certificate acknowledging the accomplishments. The members also will decide whether they want to tackle new tasks or delve more deeply into former topics.

For the next session, prepare brief descriptions of the first five selected activities to distribute among the members. This "personal workbook" can be used by the patients to take notes. You or another leader can "sign off" each individual's activities upon completion. This gives members a concrete record of their progress.

38 Individual GIT Goal Plans

Therapeutic Rationale
This project forces members to formulate short-term goals and to translate them into measurable forms. The task helps patients focus on behavioral steps needed to achieve desired changes.

Materials
goal plan sheet (see sample following this task)
pens or pencils

Procedure
Begin with a general discussion about how people can increase their happiness by learning how to make small changes in doing specific things. You might offer that it is sometimes difficult to know where to start making changes, but a good way to begin is to sit down and think about the specific things a person might want to do differently. State that it is *not* a good idea to try to change too many things all at once; that it's better to do a little bit at a time. Distribute goal plan sheets and encourage members to select an area on which they would most like to work. You and the other leaders can work individually with members to help them put their goals into specific, behavioral language (care should be taken here). Also, state how the patients will measure their own progress. Finally, list the GIT members who will work to help the patients accomplish their objectives.

39 Making Friends

Therapeutic Rationale
This activity is geared toward fostering friendships through a combination of discussion, didactic presentation, and role playing. Members explore the mutuality of friendships and increase abilities to identify with others. They learn how to express positive feelings, a process portrayed as being the "glue" that holds friendships together. After members have practiced communicating positive emotions, they learn how to initiate a new friendship and improve strategies for meeting people.

Materials
overview sheets
pens or pencils
follow-up meeting: simple refreshments

Procedure
The leader can ask an assistant to distribute

Individual Goal Plan

Name:_____   Date:_____

Area I am developing: helpfulness   ____

conversation   ____

self-care   ____

listening   ____

patience   ____

Specific target:_____

_____

How will progress be measured? _____

_____

Who will help? _____

_____

_____

_____

Overview Sheet

GIT Task 39: Making Friends

Step 1

What Do I Like in Others—What Makes Me Like Other People

Step 2

How To Help People Like Me—Expressing Positive Feelings

Step 3

Where Can I Meet People

Step 4

How To Try To Make A New Friend—
How Can I Make My Needs Known

overview sheets, or if overview sheets for this task have previously been included in individual workbooks have members turn to the appropriate page. Explain that this GIT task is designed to help members improve friendships and build new relationships. The leader can then mention that at today's meeting, each member will have a chance to share some thoughts about friendships, and that this might help in understanding their group friends better.

Begin the process by asking each participant to introduce herself or himself, for example, "Hello, I'm . . . ." Give immediate positive feedback for the desirable aspects of the introductions—"Great! You said your name really clearly"; "Terrific! You spoke up nice and loud"; "Your voice sounded friendly"; "You did a good job of looking at others while you were speaking"; etc.

Next, discuss step 1: *What do I like in others—What makes me like other people.* Solicit different views, emphasizing common features of members' responses. Highlight the notion that friends make each other feel good. Ask members to think of ways people can make one another feel good: for example, by saying positive things, listening with care, smiling, keeping eye contact, talking in a considerate fashion (not too loud or soft; not too fast), sharing things, saying funny things, and apologizing for mistakes. Again, emphasize shared responses and suggest that a meaningful way of deciding what would make other people feel good is to think about what makes you feel good.

This leads to talking about step 2: *How to help people like me—Expressing positive feelings.* You can explain that knowing how to share positive feelings is an essential communication skill. Mention that giving compliments, praise, and support can be considered as the "glue" that holds friendships together. Tell the group that expressing positive feelings requires an understanding of both *when* to praise someone and *how* to get feelings across.

To begin, you can read the following to the patients or use it as a guide when discussing *when* to praise another person.

"Praise or thank someone when they do or say something you like. Don't wait for a major accomplishment; it's important that you get in the habit of giving positive feedback to other people several times a day. People are more likely to enjoy your company if you praise or give positive feedback while the person is doing or saying something you feel good about."

Next, consider the issue of *how* to express positive feelings:

• "Make a positive verbal statement ('I like it when . . . ,' or 'I feel good when . . . ') and name what they're doing or the part of the situation that pleases you."
• "Move close to the person; you should be within three feet of the other person."
• "Look at the person; people express genuine interest in other people by making eye contact with them."
• "Smile; in giving praise, your facial gestures and body language should make it clear that you really feel good about what the person has just done."

Go around the group and ask members to express a positive feeling to the person seated to their right.

Now, discuss Step 3: *Where can I meet people.* Get members to think about the right time and place to try to meet someone new. Solicit specific ideas about good meeting circumstances familiar to members. Encourage more socially effective members to share advice with less outgoing members, for example, "What are some of your secrets?" Ask members to relate how they feel when talking to someone new, and highlight commonalities between different members.

Finally, have the group consider Step 4: *How can I make my needs known.* Begin by reviewing the following simple formula for starting a conversation.

- *Greeting* new person and making eye contact
- Making *small talk* (for example, about the weather or anything both participants have in common)
- *Listening* to response
- *Expressing* any positive feeling
- *Leaving the door open* for next meeting.

Have members take turns role playing a situation in which they are approaching someone for the first time. Discuss what to do if the person is unfriendly, and help members realize that even though they can't control other people's reactions, they can try to get a new friendship started.

In order to practice their new skills, ask members to try to make a new friend before the next meeting, and to invite the new acquaintance to the meeting. At this follow-up meeting, have each member introduce the friend to the rest of the group. A leader can tell the newcomers a bit about the GIT group, and solicit reactions to the friendship exercise. If members relate failure in attempting new relationships, the leader can try to allay any negative feelings by reminding the members that even though they weren't totally successful, they did give it a try. Portray attempting to meet people as valuable in and of itself. The leader may want to mention that there are no absolute "guarantees" and that everybody has had experiences where friendliness didn't immediately pay off, but in the long run the skills they are developing will produce greater social successes.

40 Television Decisions

Therapeutic Rationale
Television offers many patients a valuable leisure resource. Learning how to select appropriate programs accurately, interpret televised messages, and negotiate viewing conflicts with other patients can all help members to enjoy and learn from television more completely. This activity also develops reading and time-telling skills, and helps patients recognize the value of planning and communication.

Materials
current local television schedule (from the newspaper or *TV Guide*)
paper and writing implements
television

Procedure
Begin by asking the members what they like about television and by making a list of their favorite TV programs. Ask how often members currently watch television, and whether they enjoy the programs. You can ask if any ever watch something they really don't enjoy, simply because someone else turned it on. Elicit comments about uncertainty in expressing opinions and handling conflicts when disagreements arise over another's program choice. Ask if patients ever miss favorite programs because of forgetfulness—the time and channel.

Talk about any shared TV interests among members (maybe several enjoy music and dancing programs such as "Dancing on Air"; some may like detective shows, news programs, or comedies). Mention types of programs that patients may never have tried watching, for example, cooking or gardening educational program. Ask members if they've ever learned anything from television. This can lead to a discussion about the kinds of misinformation television can provide: exaggerated views of violence from news programs; false beliefs about products from advertisements; unrealistic expectations about family harmony from situation comedies, etc.

The leader can have patients suggest a program that the group could watch together.

While watching the program, the leader can point out and attempt to clarify confusing TV messages. Encourage opinions about the program and advertisements. Viewers should begin to understand the purpose of television advertising, and recognize how advertisers sometimes try to make people feel inadequate in order to sell a particular product.

Later, members can discuss how a group of people can decide what to watch on a communal TV when everyone has different preferences. Role playing can serve to help individuals learn how to voice their preferences, and give practice in suggesting ways to compromise, for example, "You can watch your favorite program first, if I can have my choice next."

Finally, participants can decide on one or two programs they will try to watch during the next week. Have members consult the local TV schedule to find out the time and channel. At the next meeting, ask members to report on their success in:

1. remembering the program
2. remembering the program time
3. remembering the program channel or consulting the schedule
4. assertively asking to view their program
5. what they liked about the show, if they watched the program, and whether they plan to view it again.

41   Relaxation Training

Therapeutic Rationale
Learning how to manage the stress response is of utmost importance for chronically mentally ill patients. These patients can benefit from training that elicits a more calm and controlled reaction to threatening and upsetting events. Members are introduced to both muscle relaxation and self-talk techniques for relaxation.

Materials
overview sheets

Procedure
You can read the following or use it as a reference when discussing relaxation techniques with members.

How Do I Feel When I am Tense
"Many people do not realize which parts of their bodies are chronically tense. Relaxation training provides a way of telling where you are tense.

"Sit back for a moment and review your inner feelings. Is your neck tight or loose? Sometimes a good way of discovering where you carry tension is to try to tighten up particular muscle groups and then let go of the tension. If you then feel very different than you did before this exercise, it is likely that you were tensing that area of your body, maybe without even realizing it!

"To begin, tense your hands by making tight fists and holding them for the count of five. Now release the tension. Do your hands feel looser and more comfortable?

"Next, tighten your neck by pushing your chin to your chest. Hold your head down in a strained position for the count of five. Now relax. Does your neck feel more relaxed than usual?

"Finally, tense your shoulders and upper back, moving them up toward your ears. Hold this position for five counts. Now let your shoulders fall back. Does this part of your body feel different?

"These exercises can help you test where your muscles typically get tense. Different people get tense in different ways."

Deciding if I Want To Relax
"There are some times when you might especially want to help yourself feel more relaxed. Think about the situations where you would most like to be more relaxed, for example: at bedtime; when you're afraid, when you're angry. Learning how to relax is a skill

that can come in handy at lots of different times. Once you know how to make yourself calm, you can choose when to use this ability."

Techniques To Help Me Relax

1. Muscle Relaxation

"You cannot have warm, peaceful feelings in your body if you are experiencing psychological stress. Relaxing your muscles reduces pulse rate, blood pressure, and breathing rate. Muscle relaxation can be practiced to reduce anxiety and stress.

"This method of relaxation is based on the idea that the body responds to anxiety-provoking thoughts and events with muscle tension. The tension increases the person's feeling of anxiety. Muscle relaxation reduces the body's tension and helps decrease anxiety. Learning to keep your body loose and relaxed can keep you from feeling tense. These methods can help you get to sleep and stay calm in tough situations. It will take some time to get good at relaxing your muscles, but the effort is well worth it."

As the leader, you can then read or play a tape with instructions like the following:

"In order to learn how to truly relax, you must first learn to vividly recognize the difference between what it feels like to be relaxed and what it feels like to be tense. To do this you are going to alternate between tensing and relaxing various muscle groups, feeling the difference each time. You will also learn how to breathe properly, since breathing is an important part of learning how to relax. OK, make yourself comfortable. If you are wearing any tight-fitting clothing, such as a necktie or a tightly-buttoned collar, loosen these so you are more comfortable. If you are wearing a sweater and are too warm, you may want to remove the sweater so you are more comfortable. Rest your arms in your lap or on the arms of the chair.

"Take a deep breath, exhale slowly, and let yourself settle deeply into the chair. Your arms are resting comfortably . . . your legs are resting and slightly spread apart. Your eyes are gently closed as you sink down into the chair. Your jaw is slightly slack.

"When you exhale, let the air out slowly. You are settled into the chair and each time you exhale, let yourself settle just a little more deeply into the support of the chair.

"Your entire interest is focused on my voice as it guides you to relax. You are simply waiting for and carefully listening to my voice. Keep breathing normally, letting the air flow out slowly.

"On the next breath, breathe a little deeper than before, and let it out slowly again. Good. Keep breathing slowly and normally. On the next breath, breathe even deeper than before and hold it for about seven seconds, then let it out slowly. Good. . . . Breathe normally and slowly . . . quietly.

"Let your entire body fall a little more into your chair. Now allow your attention to review your entire body. You are listening to my voice and becoming aware of your whole body there in the chair . . . the back of your neck, your ears and scalp, your face, your nose, your throat and shoulders, your back pressing into the support of the chair, the weight of your hips and legs, your ankles and feet.

"There is nothing to change. You are merely observing . . . experiencing the different parts of your body . . .

"In a moment I am going to ask you to slowly begin to tense up, step-by-step, certain muscles in your body, for about five to ten seconds each time. At the end of the five to ten seconds, I will then say the word "relax." When I do, I want you to *quickly* release the tension in the muscles, and again immediately relax, throwing away the tension the instant that I say the word "relax," and begin to breathe slowly and deeply again.

"Begin with both hands, begin to slowly, step-by-step, tighten up your muscles by making a fist, and hold it there. Feel the tension in your fingers build . . . in your knuckles . . .

feel it spread to your forearms, building, hold your breath . . . ready, RELAX, exhaling slowly. Notice the contrast as the tension dissolves, running out from your hands. Stay relaxed and take a deep breath, letting it flow out slowly. As the air flows out, the tension dissolves. The contrast is restful . . . peaceful . . . deeply restful.

"Simply become aware of your entire body again, totally relaxed, heavy and slowed down. In a moment, I am going to ask you to tense another muscle group. Tense these muscles when you are asked to do so, but tense *only* the muscles described. Do not attempt to tense any other muscles, unless you are asked to do so.

"Now slowly bend your arms at your elbows until they can bend no further and make them tense and tight. Do not tense any other muscles except for your arm muscles. Keep trying to build them further than they can go. Study the tight, uncomfortable feelings in both your upper arms and your forearms. Ready, RELAX. Immediately allow your hands to fall back down. Again, notice the difference between tension and relaxation. Feel the tension flow out of your arms as you again become totally relaxed and slowed down. Breathe slowly and smoothly, you are calm and at peace.

"Now slowly arch your shoulders back; try to touch your shoulder blades together. Feel the tenseness in your shoulders; how the muscles are pulling tight. Ready, RELAX. Feel the tightness run right off your back and shoulders. Become aware of how different and more loose your shoulders are now, how relaxed your back is now. The tenseness is fading away and you are again completely relaxed in your shoulders and in your back . . . completely relaxed and smooth like the rest of your body. Breathe deeply and smoothly, exhaling slowly . . . and relax.

"Now, slowly roll your head on the axis of your neck three or so times in one direction, then in the opposite direction while tens-ing your neck muscles. Feel them tighten up. One way and then the other. Ready, RELAX. Feel the muscles of your neck become loose and relaxed, as the tension disappears and fades away. Feel the difference . . . you are now relaxed again, totally. Your entire body is heavy, relaxed, and slowed down. All your muscles are loose. You are breathing slowly, exhaling slowly, breathing very, very smoothly.

"Now, slowly tense your muscles in your forehead. Frown, so that your forehead wrinkles and you knit your brows. Feel the skin on your forehead pull. Ready, RELAX. Let the tense feeling run off of your forehead and feel your forehead become smooth and relaxed. Notice the difference between tension and relaxation. You are totally relaxed again, restful, and slowed down. You are calm and your breathing is smooth, and you are relaxed.

"Now slowly tense your cheeks. Squint your eyes and pull back hard on the corners of your mouth, as if you were smiling really hard. Feel how uncomfortable it is, how tense. Ready, RELAX. Stop squinting and let your face totally relax like the rest of your body. Feel the tightness run off. Your face is smooth and relaxed. Continue to breathe slowly and smoothly. Your entire body is relaxed and calm.

"Now, together concentrate on your hands, your arms, your shoulders, your neck, your forehead, and your face and eyes. Slowly tense up all the muscles in these areas . . . your hands, your arms, your neck, your shoulders, and your face. Make sure your stomach and the rest of you are relaxed. Ready, RELAX. Let all the tension drain off into the air completely. Notice how different it feels, how much more relaxed and calm your face, arms, hands, neck, and shoulders feel. Breathe deeply and slowly. You are comfortable and relaxed.

"In a moment, the relaxation procedure will be finished. Explore your body from your feet up. Make sure every muscle is relaxed . . . First your toes and your feet . . . your legs,

Overview Sheet

GIT Task 41: Relaxation Training

How I Can Help Myself Feel Relaxed

How Do I Feel When I Am Tense?

Deciding If I Want To Relax

Techniques To Help Me Relax

- *Muscle Relaxation*
- *Calming Self-Talk*

very relaxed . . . your thighs . . . stomach . . . shoulders . . . all very relaxed . . . your arms . . . your neck and face . . . and finally your forehead . . . all are relaxed now.

"Just sit there and feel very relaxed, noticing the warmness of the relaxation. Your breathing is slow and steady. I would like you to stay this way for about one more minute, and then I am going to count to five. (one minute pause)

"In a moment I am going to count to five . . . When I reach the count of five, I want you to open your eyes, feeling very calm and refreshed . . . One . . . feeling very calm; . . . Two . . . very calm, very refreshed; Three . . . very refreshed; Four . . . and Five.

(pause) "You will want to practice these steps to muscle relaxation between meetings. Select a quiet place where you can sit comfortably, undisturbed."

2. Calming Self-Talk

"Scientific research has indicated that if you tell yourself that a certain situation . . . any situation at all . . . will be uncomfortable, your muscles will immediately start to become tense, your heart will begin to beat faster, you will begin to perspire, and you will become anxious, sometimes even before you are actually in the situation. Further, when actually in a situation . . . almost any situation . . . if you tell yourself that the situation will be uncomfortable and frightening, your heart will immediately begin to beat faster, you will become anxious and tense, and you will feel uncomfortable in the situation.

"Your view of situations determine how you *feel* in these situations. The way you *think* and the things you tell yourself help to create your emotional reaction. Luckily, your perceptions are under your control. By learning to change your perceptions by thinking positively, you can change your emotional reactions to situations and learn to become less frightened or anxious.

"Negative thinking can make you feel very scared, even in a safe situation. On the other hand, positive thinking can make you feel more comfortable and relaxed, whether you are in a safe or difficult situation. Your thoughts can influence what you actually feel. Positive thinking can help you cope.

"Today you will learn how to use positive coping statements in conjunction with the relaxation technique you have been practicing. You will learn to concentrate upon positive self-statements, which will deepen your relaxation by altering your own feelings. Together, using the muscle relaxation technique and positive self-coping statements, you will be able to relax far beyond that which you can imagine.

"To learn to talk to yourself positively, you must first become aware of the kind of negative, self-defeating statements you think of when you are faced with a difficult situation. Most people feel anxious because of negative statements they make to themselves such as

- 'I know I won't be able to deal with this.'
- 'I am becoming more afraid, and now I can't relax.'
- 'I can't face this, it might hurt too much.'
- 'I'm so afraid of what might happen here, I must leave.'

"These negative self-statements occur silently and make you feel tense and anxious. The way you think to yourself can make you feel worse.

"When you face a tough situation, what sort of thoughts run through your head? You may be using self-defeating thoughts that increase your discomfort, such as 'I can't handle this,' and you make yourself become anxious. Your muscles become tense and you actually increase your perception of discomfort. By changing these negative statements, you can improve the situation so that it is not as bad. Try and think up some positive thoughts you might use to fight off those self-defeating statements . . . What might you say to yourself instead? You might try saying things such as

- 'I can cope with this . . . it's going to be easy.'
- 'This will be OK.'
- 'This will only take a few minutes.'
- 'Everything is going to be fine.'
- 'The more I relax, the more comfortable I'll be.'
- 'I'm doing great . . . think positive.'

"What you are now learning to do is to substitute positive self-statements in place of negative self-statements. You are learning to stop thinking negatively when dealing with situations.

"In the middle of difficult situations, practice saying things like

- 'I've got it now . . . I'm in control.'
- 'That's the way . . . good.'
- 'It's almost over.'
- 'I'm doing great here.'

"Learning how to think positively when you are finished dealing with a difficult situation is also important. You should assure yourself that you have coped effectively with self-statements such as

- 'I did it!!!'
- 'It's all over!!!'
- 'That was quick and easy!'
- 'I did a good job.'
- 'I was in control!'

"Thinking more positively takes practice. At first, just work to become more aware of your negative thinking. Next, practice forcing yourself to stop self-defeating thought patterns. Last, try to substitute more constructive ways of thinking like those described earlier."

42 Telephone Calls and Listening Skills

Therapeutic Rationale

This activity helps to develop basic communication skills central to effective interpersonal relationships. In addition, members acquire greater familiarity with telephone use: practicing dialing, answering, and conversation skills. Improved telephone skills translate to more effective and independent use of hospital and community resources and better maintenance of outside relationships. These skills also provide members with a chance to assist busy staff personnel when phone lines ring simultaneously.

Materials
overview sheets
local telephone book
copies of personal phone book pages
stapler
pens or pencils
an operational telephone

Procedure
Ask members about their typical use of the telephone. Do they make calls regularly, receive calls regularly, answer the phone for others, feel awkward or uncomfortable when talking on the phone, know how to say goodbye, know their phone number, know how to use the phone book? Let members know that anyone can learn to be a better conversationalist, and that this GIT task will let them practice important communication skills. Explain that the group will first discuss how to be a better listener and then practice specific telephone skills.

Step 1
Provide a rationale for step 1. Tell members that active listening skills improve relationships by boosting the speaker's self-esteem (for example, "It feels great to know someone cares enough to listen carefully.") and make communication more clear between people. Explain that this helps to reduce conflicts and avoid the arguments and tension that misunderstandings produce. Inform members that knowing how to listen attentively will help all relationships. You can point out that

learning how to absorb what another person is saying takes patience and practice, because people are often all too eager to present their own views.

Next, discuss the five practical steps for improving one's listening skills noted on the overview sheet following this task.

Members can break into pairs and take turns role playing listener and speaker.

Participants can be encouraged to give one another supportive feedback after these exercises by asking the speakers:

"Did the listener make you feel comfortable?" or "Did the listener seem to be interested in what you were saying?"

Step 2

Begin with a discussion of when it is appropriate to make telephone calls, such as the times of day when people are likely to be in and available to talk on the phone. Next, ask members why they make calls (for example, to share information, give support, feel close to others, etc.). The group can then list features of a good phone call, for example, it's not too long, the party gets to the point, the caller had a clear purpose in mind before calling, etc. The group can then practice dialing numbers to make sure all members are comfortable with the type of phone that is available (rotary dial or touch). Be sure to give members practice with using alphabetical as well as numerical phone codes.

The group can practice dialing emergency numbers (fire and medical) with the phone disengaged, and can discuss when it is appropriate to make such calls.

Direct a discussion of how to answer and receive calls for others. Ask members if they ever resent being interrupted by a phone call. Practice role playing a friendly way of answering the phone—"Hello, this is _____. May I help you?" Finally, help members discuss

assertive ways of concluding a phone conversation that's running too long. "Well, it was good to hear from you. I need to get going, but thanks for calling. Goodbye." or "Well, it was nice talking. I need to get going now. I'm glad I was able to reach you. Goodbye."

Step 3

This step involves practice in finding telephone numbers. Ask members if they know their number; if they don't know their number, encourage them to find it out and try to memorize it. Then take out a local directory and ask the group to locate some preselected numbers. Have members imagine different situations that might arise in the community and find numbers of services they might need. Role play methods of coping with each of the following situations:

• making a dentist appointment (ask about fees, insurance coverage, etc.)
• calling the community mental health center to reschedule an appointment
• calling to find out when a store is open
• calling to arrange for a bus schedule to be sent to you
• calling to find out what hours the local library is open

Ask members to find numbers in the directory and dial (using a disconnected phone). After completing these scenes, have members generate other circumstances that call for telephone use.

Finally, distribute individual phone book pages and have members staple their own personal telephone books for future use. As a follow-up, encourage members to report on any successful calls they make.

Overview Sheet

GIT Task 42: Telephone Calls and Listening Skills

Step 1: Active Listening Skills

1. Make good eye contact with the speaker.

2. Lean toward the speaker.

3. Nod your head and say "uh-huh" occasionally to let the speaker know that you are hearing what is being said.

4. Ask questions that help the speaker expand on what is being expressed.

5. At the end, reflect back, using similar words, what you have just heard: "I hear you saying that _____. Is that right?"

Step 2: Using the Telephone

- When and why to call
- What makes a good phone call?
- Dialing
- Receiving calls
- How to end a phone conversation politely

Step 3: Finding Telephone Numbers

- What is my number?
- Using the phone directory
- Keeping track of phone numbers

43   Self-Report Questionnaires

Therapeutic Rationale

In the past when conducting program evaluations, hospital personnel found that many patients enjoyed completing self-report inventories. It seemed that members welcomed the opportunity to think about and to express their attitudes, feelings, and beliefs in a formal manner. Completing such questionnaires provides chances for self-discovery and can foster the development of insight and self-awareness. It was also discovered that the peer rating scale can be used to help group members articulate feelings toward peers. This facilitates a mutual feedback process which can help members learn from one another and recognize the impact of their behavior on others.

Materials

Brief self-report questionnaire (see sample). Either the test's language should be relatively simple or enough extra leaders should be on hand to read and interpret items for group

Inpatient Locus of Control Scale (Templin & Chambliss, 1980)

1. Do you feel there is little you can do to improve your performance on games you play?

2. Do you have a lot of choice about who your friends are on the ward?

3. Do you feel that some patients get special treatment from staff members for no reason?

4. Do you feel that working hard will help you get money?

5. Do you feel that problems you have with medication will eventually get better on their own?

6. Do you feel that planning ahead will help you budget your limited number of cigarettes?

7. Do you feel only lucky people get as much coffee as they want?

8. Do you feel that you have to try hard to get better?

9. Do you feel that wishing will help you get to live in the building you desire?

10. Do you feel that you have a lot of choice in deciding what activities you do?

11. Do you feel that it doesn't pay to try hard to stop smoking because there is nothing you can do to stop?

12. Do you feel that planning ahead will help you find more interesting things to do with your free time?

13. Do you often find that wishing someone was your friend will make him or her your friend?

14. Do you feel that you can do a lot to get help for problems you have?

15. Do you feel that problems you have with people will just work themselves out?

16. Do you have to try hard to be friends with certain people who you want to be friends with?

Information About Me

Name_____

Age_____ Sex_____

Birthdate_____

Where was I born? _____

Where do I live? _____

_____

My telephone number_____

My Social Security number_____

Height_____ Weight_____

Information About People Important to Me

Name_____

Address_____

_____

Telephone number_____

Name_____

Address_____

_____

Telephone number_____

Task 43

members on a one-to-one basis. We have made use of the following:

Nowicki-Strickland Locus of Control Scale
     for Children
Moos Ward Atmosphere Scale
GIT Peer Rating Form
GIT Inpatient Locus of Control Scale

Procedure

Have an assistant distribute questionnaires at the start of the meeting. Other leaders can provide assistance to patients with limited reading abilities, and should be available to answer ambiguous questions. After members complete their self-rating form, the group can discuss the questionnaire and what it was measuring. You can use these discussions to introduce topics such as

- individual differences in people's beliefs and attitudes,
- how certain attitudes or beliefs might influence behavior,
- whether it is possible to change personal attitudes or beliefs,
- the value of self-awareness (how knowing oneself better can lead to making appropriate life choices).

44 Managing Anger

Therapeutic Rationale

Learning how to manage angry feelings more constructively can greatly improve patients' social relationships. Members are taught how to recognize their angry feelings by becoming more aware of body signals. They then practice ways of curbing impulsive responses and anger, which can often be maladaptive. Members begin to recognize their needs and to practice useful strategies to make their needs known. Constructive ways of expressing negative emotions are discussed and rehearsed. Finally, members are encouraged to

develop greater compromising skills.

Materials

overview sheets
large piece of paper and marker
blackboard and chalk

Procedure

Ask members to describe their anger experiences. Encourage patients to specify what parts of their body inform them about their own feelings. Discuss how some people respond to anger by withdrawing, whereas others act out. Explain that both "flight and fight" can be counterproductive in some situations, and give specific examples where these responses failed to resolve the problem causing the anger.

Then ask members to list situations that make them angry. Encourage specificity. Have members try to think about what was frustrating them in the anger-provoking situation. Convey the notion that since some kind of frustrated need often creates angry feelings, learning how to express and satisfy needs better can help reduce the anger.

Help members specify what they want to have happen in situations that make them angry. Present the idea that learning how to express feelings and needs assertively increases chances of having needs responded to constructively. This can lead to a discussion about how to express negative feelings.

You can explain that negative feelings—such as anger, annoyance, irritation, hurt, frustration, uneasiness, fear, sadness, and unhappiness—occur as part of normal coping with problems. Inform the group that negative feelings, when expressed directly and clearly, can be a constructive part of relationships. "We must learn how to express the negative emotions we have in constructive ways so that our relationships are strengthened, not weakened and hurtful. We should try to own up to our negative feelings, without accusing or insulting another person."

Overview Sheet

GIT Task 44: Managing Anger

What Should I Do When I Get Angry?

How Do I Usually Act When I Get Angry?

What Makes Me Angry?

What Do I Want To Happen?

How Can I Make What I Want Happen?

How To Express Negative Feelings Constructively

1. Look at the other person when you're expressing NEGATIVE FEELINGS. This helps to make your expression more direct.

2. Lean toward the person or come close to him when you are expressing NEGATIVE FEELINGS. This helps to make the expression more direct and helps the person hear correctly.

3. Have a serious expression on your face. It's important to keep your facial expression in tune with your feelings and message.

4. Use a firm tone of voice. Keep your tone of voice in touch with the feeling you are expressing.

5. State *specifically* what it is that the other person has done or said (or failed to do or say) which is producing the negative feeling in you. Be clear and specific, not vague.

6. Express yourself when the problem behavior occurs—don't wait until later.

7. Say how the person's behavior is affecting you by *owning up* to the real feelings you are experiencing. Be direct and honest about how the other person's behavior is making you feel. Don't be indirect.

8. Request that the person change his behavior or ask the person to help you try to solve the problem by coming up with alternatives.

In expressing NEGATIVE FEELINGS DIRECTLY, use phrases like:

"It really hurts my feelings when you _____. Please stop."

"When you fail to do _____, it makes me uptight and uncomfortable. I would feel much better if you would do it."

"I get so frustrated and irritated when you _____. I'd appreciate your helping me by _____."

How To Express Negative Feelings Constructively

1. Look at the other person when you're expressing *negative feelings*. This helps to make your expression more direct.

2. Lean toward the person or come close to him or her when you express *negative feelings*. This helps to make the expression more direct and helps the person hear correctly.

3. Have a serious expression on your face. It's important to keep your facial expression in tune with feelings and message.

4. Use a firm tone of voice. Keep tone of voice in touch with the feeling you are expressing.

5. State *specifically* what it is that the other person has done or said (or failed to do or say) that is producing the negative feeling in you. Be clear and specific, not vague.

6. Express yourself when the problem behavior occurs—don't wait until later.

7. Say how the person's behavior is affecting you by *owning up* to the real feelings you are experiencing. Be direct and honest about how the other person's behavior is making you feel. Don't be indirect.

8. Request that the person change his or her behavior or ask the person to help you try to solve the problem by coming up with alternatives.

In expressing *negative feelings directly,* use phrases like:

- "It really hurts my feelings when you _____. Please stop."

- "When you fail to do _____, it makes me uptight and uncomfortable. I would feel much better if you would do it."

- "I get so frustrated and irritated when you _____. I'd appreciate your helping me by _____."

Suggest ways of compromising with the other person, such as "I feel ignored when you change the channel on the radio while I'm listening to it. I understand that you like to listen to your favorite music, but maybe we can make a deal. After fifteen minutes, I'll give you a turn to listen to your channel."

All group leaders can demonstrate effective expression of angry feelings in a role playing experience. Then patients can be encouraged to role play different situations calling for assertive self-expression of anger. You can conclude by emphasizing the idea that expressing *negative feelings directly* will help solve relationship problems by getting them out in the open in honest, clear, and constructive ways. Tell members *not* to let tensions and dissatisfactions build up and simmer; they will eventually come out in harmful and indirect ways that will make problem-solving more difficult.

45   Looking My Best

Therapeutic Rationale
Because personal appearance shapes social reaction, it is important for members to learn how to present themselves appropriately. This activity emphasizes personal responsibility for self-care and provides learning experiences to support greater attentiveness to appearance.

Materials
copies of "Things To Do" sheet
nail polish and remover
shoe polish and rags

Procedure
The leader can begin by asking members: "Why is it important to look my best?" Members can be encouraged to generate various reasons; for example, to feel better, happier, and more confident, to make a better impression on others, etc. You can distribute magazine pictures representing good and bad appearances. The group can review the pictures and share what is good and bad and the reasons why.

Next, you can focus on the question: "What can I do to look my best?" The group can generate a list, which can be typed and

Things To Do	How Often	Supplies I Need
Shower or Bathe		
Deodorant		
Brush Teeth		
Use Mouthwash		
Wash Face		
Use Makeup		
Shave		
Shampoo Hair		
Comb Hair		
Trim Hair		
Trim Fingernails		
Trim Toenails		
Wear Clean and Neat Clothes		
Wear Appropriate Clothes		
Wear Appropriate Jewelry		
Wear Clean Shoes		
Wear Clean Stockings		
Stand Up Straight		
Smile! Smile! Smile!		

Task 45

distributed at the following meeting to review and to discuss how often each grooming activity needs to be performed (see sample). When possible, the behaviors talked about can be modeled.

Encourage the group to discuss what supplies they need to look their best. Use the group-generated list of grooming activities to talk about supplies needed. Members often enjoy sharing views on specific brands.

You can suggest to members what can be done to look even better. Participants can be asked to discuss one way in which their appearance could be improved, for example, the female members can paint their nails and the men can polish their shoes. The next session can be an occasion where all members would come looking their best. At this later meeting, each member can be asked to stand while the group recognizes the good aspects of the appearance. If possible, you or another leader can arrange for a beautician to come and discuss grooming. This individual can outline any opportunities available in the hospital to improve grooming. Arrangements can be made for the group can accompany the leader on a trip to the hospital beauty shop, where hair styling or a facial can be demonstrated on a member.

46   Meal Planning and Cookbook

Therapeutic Rationale
This activity provides practice in organizing meals, and leads to putting together a group cookbook, especially useful to members after they leave the hospital. The task helps patients plan for cooking responsibilities, and gives insight into practical approaches to planning meals suitable to the budget and patience constraints of most newly discharged patients. The experience also fosters a sense of belonging and shared purpose.

Materials
overview sheets	8 ½″ × 11″ construction paper
index cards	
pens and pencils	stapler
magazines	copies of recipe
scissors	pages

Procedure
Begin by asking members to talk about foods especially good for them to eat. A review of the four basic food groups discussed at an earlier meeting may be helpful. Present the idea of including food items from all four groups at each meal. Ask members if they think it will always be possible to do this. Since many members may find themselves eating alone after discharge and living on a tight budget with limited cooking supplies and shopping opportunities, it may be inappropriate to insist on three square meals each day. Instead, emphasize the desirability of balanced nutrition over the course of a day or two.

Next, have members talk about foods they enjoy that are simple to prepare and don't require much cleanup. Discuss which foods are easiest to cook for one person. Also, have members consider the recipes that don't generate lots of leftovers and call for too many fresh ingredients. Ask participants to share their cooking successes—what great meals they have fixed. Have the group generate a list of possible recipes to use in a cookbook. Include several entrees, vegetables, and dessert suggestions, and have the group vote on the three most popular main courses, vegetables, and desserts. If possible, select some foods appropriate for breakfast, lunch, and dinner. Then, have the group plan three sample meals using these foods.

Menu Suggestions
macaroni and cheese	hamburger
green beans or peas	pasta salad
canned fruit	cookies

Overview Sheet

GIT Task 46: Meal Planning and Cookbook

What Should I Eat?

What Are Good Things for Me to Eat?

How Can I Plan My Meals?

How To Fix Good Meals for Myself.

spaghetti   hot dogs
green salad   baked beans
canned fruit   fresh fruit

scrambled eggs   cereal
tomato juice   milk
toast   orange juice

french toast
maple syrup

Begin making a group cookbook using the three selected meals. Start by writing out a shopping list including specific brands and item sizes, if possible. Have members estimate the cost of the ingredients. Write down the recipes for each food item, including information on bowls, pans, and utensils needed. You can have these recipe pages copied before the next meeting.

Ask an assistant to distribute recipe pages and construction paper. Have the members staple pages to create their own cookbooks. Use magazine cutouts or hand-drawn designs to illustrate each of the three featured meals.

47 When I Get a Cold

Therapeutic Rationale
This activity helps to develop self-care skills and foster members' sense of independence. Since outbreaks of colds are very common among patients living in close quarters, most patients will readily identify with this task. It emphasizes the importance of personal responsibility for health care and builds feelings of self-efficacy. Members also acquire information useful in helping and supporting others who are sick. By building awareness of how cold viruses are spread, this activity may help curb contagion among members.

Materials
overview sheets
magazines with ads for nonprescription cold
  medications
copies of "When I Get Cold" sheet
disposable thermometers

Procedure
After everyone has turned to their overview sheet, ask if any members have colds at the moment. By responding with a sympathetic, caring statement to those suffering from colds, you, as the leader, serve as a model for appropriately expressing concern.

The group can list cold symptoms on their sheets. After the major cold signs have been reviewed, consider each symptom in turn and list possible treatments. Discuss why different methods of treatment work. Ask members which treatment they prefer. Be careful to discuss the specific steps involved in each treatment: where to obtain medicine while in the hospital, where to purchase Tylenol in the community, how to read a thermometer, and what medications some patients should avoid, for example, certain over-the-counter cold preparations should not be taken by patients on certain antidepressants and neuroleptic drugs.

Members often enjoy discussing their favorite cold remedies and memories of mother's chicken soup. Sometimes participants will debate the best brands of nonprescription cold remedies. Have the group look through magazines in order to read advertisements for different medications. Discuss the relative expense of various products. Point out that some of the most expensive preparations may suppress symptoms, but don't really speed recovery. Add that some of these remedies can leave people feeling very drowsy and "wiped out." You might suggest that for some people taking it easy, drinking lots of fluids, and just relaxing when they have a cold may be as effective as taking many costly drugs.

Ask members when they think a doctor should be consulted. Discuss the kinds of symptoms that would warrant seeking medical attention, for example, high fever, deep cough that lasts too long, etc. Mention physical conditions that might make a person more vulner-

Overview Sheet

GIT Task 47: When I Get a Cold

What Are the Signs That I Am Getting a Cold?

What Can I Do To Feel Better?

What Supplies Do I Need? How Do I Get Them?

When Should I Contact a Doctor?

When I Get a Cold

Signs of a Cold	What I Can Do To Feel Better— Supplies I Might Need
Runny Nose/Sneezing	Take medicine, nose drops or spray, tissues
Cough	Cough drops, syrup, Vicks rub
Fever	Thermometer, aspirin, Tylenol, rest, stay in bed, liquids to prevent dehydration, Vitamin C
Chills	Rest, blanket, aspirin, hot tea and lemon
Sore throat, hoarseness	Gargle with salt and water; use throat lozengers, throat spray
Aching muscles	Rest, stay warm, use BenGay
Frozen feet	Soak feet; use warm socks, heating pad, hot water bottle

Task 47

able to serious negative cold reactions. Discuss the things that might happen during a medical exam and instruments that the physician might use during the examination.

Start a discussion of how to help a friend or roommate who has a cold. Emphasize the need to be patient with someone who is feeling badly, and how much a person appreciates a show of concern during illness. Discuss how friends can reciprocate caring.

End by presenting strategies for preventing colds. Mention the importance of such measures as staying rested, dry, and warm; eating properly; getting adequate amounts of vitamin C in diet; avoiding hand contact with contagious people; etc. Discuss how covering a person's mouth when sneezing and coughing, not sharing cups or utensils, and washing hands regularly are all good ways to minimize chances of spreading cold germs.

48 Graduation

Therapeutic Rationale
This graduation tradition provides members and leaders with a sense of completion and closure. It affords formal recognition of the group members' shared accomplishments.

Materials and Procedure
Same as GIT Task 12, except former graduates who remember the procedure may be asked to take a more active role in organizing the graduation room and ceremony.

GIT Module V: Tasks 49–60

---

49 Introductions

Therapeutic Rationale
Same as GIT Task 37, except former members who remember the procedure can be given a greater role in organizing the meeting.

50 Cheap Treats and Snacks

Therapeutic Rationale
A great majority of patients have limited monetary funds and limitless appetites for snacks. This two-part activity allows the group to tackle the problem this poses collectively, to generate possible solutions, and to demonstrate preparing some edible treats. The task expands members' cooking repertoire, provides ideas for aftercare, and builds awareness of budgeting and dietary issues. Members take pleasure in successful food preparation, and enjoy serving their creations to other patients.

Materials
menu planning session:
 large piece of paper
 marker
 copies of recipes (see sample at the end of this task)
snack preparation session:
 copies of selected recipes
 stapler
 paper
 markers or crayons
 ingredients for one or two selected snacks

Procedure
Menu Planning Session
You can get members to list their favorite snack foods and when they like to enjoy

Snack Recipe Ideas

1. Cheese Stuffed Potatoes

Ingredients:
12 to 15 potatoes (aluminum foil
    will retain heat)
1 jar Cheez Whiz
large mixing bowl
knife, fork, and spoon

Method:
1. cut potatoes in half, lengthwise
2. scoop out potato pulp with
   spoon; put in bowl
3. combine potatoes and cheese
   spread
4. mash with fork until mixture is
   smooth
5. fill potato skins with mixture
6. serve and enjoy this inexpensive
   and nutritious snack

2. Onion Dip

Ingredients:
sour cream
tofu
package of dehydrated onion soup
    mix
toast (for dipper; may also use chips
    or pretzels)
knife, bowl, and fork

Method:
1. mash tofu with sour cream until
   smooth
2. add onion soup mix; stir with
   fork until smooth
3. if possible, refrigerate for two
   hours
4. cut each piece of toast lengthwise
   into 5 or 6 dippers
5. serve dippers with onion dip

3. Popcorn

Ingredients:
popcorn
air popcorn popper
mixed seasonings, salt substitute, or
    butter flavored salt

Method:
1. plug in air popper
2. put in popcorn
3. add seasonings to popped corn

special treats, for example, when with friends, at parties, while relaxing, etc. Ask participants if they think snacks are good or bad for them. Patients can be encouraged to discuss the pros and cons of snacking and to consider inexpensive, nutritious snack possibilities that the group can prepare. After soliciting snack ideas, you (or an assistant with legible handwriting) can list possibilities on a large piece of paper. Ask members if they'd be interested in preparing a short recipe book of snacks for themselves to use after discharge. Vote on which recipes to include, noting the most popular choice. Have an assistant carefully print any new recipes generated by members. (The group may want to include the snack recipes listed in this book.)

Snack Preparation Session
(If members can travel together to the store to purchase ingredients ahead of the group meeting time, all the better!)

An assistant can distribute copies of selected recipes along with a blank sheet of paper to use as a cover. A stapler can be passed while you demonstrate how to fasten the pages to form a book. Members can discuss possible titles for their book, and decorate their covers however they want.

Next, have members turn to the most popular recipe. Place on the table a grocery bag containing the ingredients and utensils listed in the recipe. Ask for a volunteer to direct the actions. Assist members in following the recipe. After members have sampled the snack and expressed opinions, encourage them to share leftovers with other patients.

51   Getting Along With Roommates

Therapeutic Rationale
The activity is designed to foster better relationships with roommates. Group members become more sensitive to others and improve strategies for resolving interpersonal conflicts. Members identify areas they may need to work on in order to become better roommates themselves. Role playing gives members practice in more assertive ways of handling disagreements.

Materials
overview sheets
copies of "Different Ways People Can Be" sheets
pens or pencils
marker
2 large pieces of paper

Procedure
Begin by having members turn to the appropriate task overview sheet. Get the group to discuss the qualities they enjoy in a roommate and some of the advantages of living with a roommate (for example, splitting expenses, someone to talk to, someone to care about, someone to care about them, splitting chores, learning about another person's likes and dislikes, learning how to cooperate and compromise, etc.) To facilitate discussion of positive and negative roommate attributes, have a group volunteer hand out copies of the "Different Ways People Can Be" sheet that follows this task. Members can consult this list of adjectives and behaviors and talk about the desirability, undesirability, and neutrality of each item. Encourage participants to add additional roommate characteristics to this list. Make a master list of qualities the group sees as describing the ideal roommate, and another master list of annoying characteristics.

Have members consider what kind of a roommate they are to others. Ask each member to circle all of the adjectives and behaviors listed that are self-descriptive. Have them review their good qualities by comparing the items they circled with those the group listed as descriptive of a great roommate. You can identify a strength of each group member and

GIT Task 51: Getting Along With Roommates

What Are Good Things About a Roommate?

What Are Annoying Things About a Roommate?

What Are Good Things About Me?

How Can I Give Praise to Others?

What Are Annoying Things About Me?

How Can I Tell My Roommate What Bothers Me?

Different Ways People Can Be

NEAT	*TALKATIVE*
MESSY	*FRIENDLY*
SNORES	*POLITE*
SAD	*GRABBY*
GENEROUS	*CAREFUL*
SNEAKY	*ANGRY*
FAST	*SLOW*
HELPFUL	*NOSEY*
QUIET	*SMELLY*
SHARING	*SLOPPY*
WITHDRAWN	*KIND*
SMILING	*LOUD*

Task 51

reinforce his or her ideas—"This is something about you that a roommate can really appreciate." "Do you think any of your current roommates notice this about you?" "How might you help them to discover and appreciate this good quality?" Encourage supportive interactions among members by asking if they have previously had the chance to fully appreciate one another's strengths. Suggest that frequently people that live together take one another's good points for granted. Add that it is sometimes helpful to sit back and reflect on a roommate's assets and positive qualities. Explain that letting a roommate know his or her good qualities are valued can later make it easier to deal with any annoying occasions. Acknowledging positive traits and behaviors is a way of setting a favorable and supportive climate for later problem solving. Discuss strategies for expressing positive feelings about a roommate.

- Pinpoint a specific behavior to praise.
- Look at the person.
- Smile at the person.
- Get reasonably close to the person.
- Make a brief, positive verbal statement.

Members can practice giving and receiving compliments by going around the group. Ask them to try to catch each other doing or saying something nice outside the group, and then to use the techniques just practiced to express positive feelings.

Next, have members consider needed changes in themselves to become a better roommate. Ask members if they would like to report on their progress in trying to make these changes at a later session. Encourage members to pick one thing to begin working on that could improve their roommate relationships. You can go around the group and have each member fill in the blank: "It's probably a little annoying sometimes when I __ _____" (make sure to have all the group leaders take a turn at identifying a negative personal quality).

Focus on techniques useful in resolving roommate conflicts. Review with members the following problem-solving sequence.

1. Pinpoint the problem.
2. Decide how the problem makes you feel.
3. Decide what you would prefer to see change.
4. Express your feelings and preference clearly.
5. Listen and reflect back to each other.
6. Generate alternative solutions or remedies.
7. Decide what is the best compromise.
8. Decide together how to carry out this compromise.
9. Give praise to one another for negotiating.
10. Praise one another for carrying out the plan.

Emphasize that expressing feelings, making appropriate requests, asking for cooperation, and agreeing upon a compromise are all effective strategies for resolving roommate problems. Ask the group to think about techniques that often fail to work—confronting roommates in an angry, blaming, and belittling manner; walking away and avoiding a major problem; running to staff members before trying to work out a minor difference with the roommate; etc.

Members can then role play the following situations, possibly by having all the leaders begin with the *wrong way* of doing it, then having members identify why that approach was unsuccessful, and finally having a patient member try to deal with the situation more constructively.

- Person changes TV channel without permission.
- Person interrupts a quiet conversation.
- Roommate opens windows without asking.
- Roommate eats special snacks you had saved.
- Person spits on the floor.
- Roommate leaves dirty laundry on floor.
- Roommate borrowed something without asking.

- Roommate criticizes your taste in clothes.
- Roommate refuses to share snack with you.
- Roommate lies about where they were going.

You can conclude this task with a discussion of how to handle really serious roommate difficulties that require outside assistance. Not all problems can be solved, even though most roommate problems can be reduced. Have the group recognize that some problems, for example, chronic roommate stealing, substance abuse, violence, failure to take prescribed medication, do demand outside help.

52 Shopping for My Needs

Therapeutic Rationale
This experience helps members recognize their material needs and develop appropriate strategies for meeting these needs independently. The task builds a sense of personal efficacy. Members practice planning for shopping excursions and use role playing exercises to become more comfortable with various purchasing situations. This part of the task helps build social skills which enhance the probability of successful buying experiences in the community.

Materials
overview sheets
play money to use during role playing
local bus and train schedules
copies of a local area map

Procedure
After all members have turned to their overview sheet, discuss different types of shopping that members currently do and types they may need to do once they leave the hospital, for example, food, clothes, shoes, hardware,

pharmacy, browsing. Have members share their *best* and *worst* shopping experiences. Discuss what made these excursions successful or unsuccessful—planning versus disorganization; good luck versus bad luck; having plenty of time versus being rushed; etc.

Now have members think about their needs. Discuss when there is a need to buy new clothes and shoes, and the things a person needs to know before going shopping (size, brand, and color). Have members discuss how to plan food shopping, including how often trips for food need to be made, how to plan menus ahead in order to know what types of food to buy, and how the food will be stored.

You can then encourage members to think about how they plan a shopping trip. Ask how members decide on the amount of money to take shopping. Point out that this decision can help avoid budget-breaking impulse buying. Discuss how members can estimate how long a shopping trip will probably take.

Consider with members ways of arranging for transportation. Review a local bus and train schedule, demonstrating how to check for both departing and returning trip times. Use the map to indicate appropriate store locations and to chart a basic route to the store. Mention the importance of checking the weather report before making a long trip, for example, need for an umbrella if rain is forecast. Also talk about the need to plan for carrying purchases home. The group can then review the benefits of shopping alone and the advantages of shopping with a friend. Solicit different members' opinions on this one.

Ask members how they deal with sales clerks. Have the shoppers discuss how it feels when a sales clerk ignores them or is not helpful. Have the group consider ways of dealing with sales clerks in an assertive, congenial fashion. Use role playing to practice dealing with the following situations:

- asking for the location of a particular item

Overview Sheet

GIT Task 52: Shopping for My Needs

What Do I Need?

Planning a Shopping Trip

How To Deal With Sales Clerks

How To Wait in Line

How To Handle My Money

- asking for a different size or color
- asking how a garment looks
- asking for a gift box
- discovering you don't have enough money for purchase

You might also ask members to role play situations involving other shoppers. For example, have members discuss ways of dealing with these situations.

- Someone asks you for the location of an item in a store when you know where it is.
- Someone asks you for the location of an item in a store when you don't know where it is.
- Someone asks you for the location of another store when you think you know where it is.

Finally, have the group discuss how they pay for their purchases. Ask how they feel when they have to wait in a long line and how they handle it if someone asks to cut ahead of them. Discuss things that can be done to stay relaxed while waiting in a long line, and how planning ahead for plenty of time to shop can prevent any tension when making purchases takes a little longer than expected. Emphasize the notion that planning is a way of preventing stress and feelings of failure. Have members role play different situations in which they handle money to make imagined purchases. Use play money to determine what bills to give to the sales clerks for various items—for example, "If you had one $10, two $5, and five $1 bills, what would you give the clerk if you were making a $11 purchase? . . . an $18 purchase? . . . a $1.50 purchase?," etc. Have members practice making and counting change for one another; emphasize their right to take a moment to carefully count their change after receiving it.

If possible, members can take a field trip together to do some simple shopping.

53 Health Care

Therapeutic Rationale
This activity addresses members' health concerns and fosters improved prevention of health problems. The importance of compliance with psychotropic medication recommendations is explained and emphasized. Since failure of drug maintenance accounts for a majority of schizophrenic relapse cases, fostering motivation to comply with prescribed medications is vital to long-term treatment success.

Materials
overview sheets
copies of medication information sheets

Procedure
You can direct members to the appropriate task overview sheet and then lead a discussion on what it feels like when patients are at their healthiest. This can help members develop greater sensitivity to the early signs of decompensation, because they become more attuned to the subjective qualities of their experience while in a relatively good state of psychological functioning. Members also become more aware of the early warning signs of physical disorders, and as a result learn when medical attention is necessary.

Have members think about the steps they can take to become more healthy. The importance of relaxation, regular moderate exercise, rest, and a good diet can be emphasized. Members can discuss how to arrange medical and dental checkups (both in the hospital and after discharge). Explain how often patients should have preventive checkups and diagnostic tests such as PAP smears, mammograms, self-breast exams, overall physicals, etc. Also mention the importance of reduc-

Overview Sheet

GIT Task 53: Healthcare

Taking Care of My Health

How Do I Feel When I Feel Good?

What Can I Do to Feel Good?

Why Psychotropic Drugs Can Help?

Who Can Help Me Feel Good?

ing cigarette smoking, and encourage members to try to cut down on smoking. Talk about how cigarette smoking and caffeine increase the amount of antipsychotic medication patients need. By reducing their cigarette and coffee intake, patients may reduce their need for psychotropic drugs somewhat.

Open discussion about psychotropic medication. The purpose of this part of the task is to explain the effects of different drugs, and to emphasize the importance of following prescribed medication directions. You might want to read the following pages of valuable information that could be copied and distributed among the group along with their medication information sheets.

"Psychiatric drugs (which are frequently called 'psychotropic' drugs) are very helpful in the treatment of severe psychological and behavioral disorders. These types of drugs, when prescribed by your psychiatrist or physician, and taken consistently, can help improve symptoms and reduce problems that you have that affect thinking, feeling, socializing, working and playing, and caring for yourself. It is important for you to understand the usefulness and unwanted side-effects of these medications if you are taking these drugs."

Explain that this group activity is designed to give a better understanding of drug treatment.

Different Types of Psychiatric Drugs

"There are several types of drugs used in psychiatry. Each type is aimed at a specific illness or set of problems you may experience. Usually, a drug which is helpful to a person suffering from one kind of illness or disturbance is not helpful to a person suffering from a different kind of illness."

Now you can go over the list of some common psychiatric drugs and the illnesses the drugs are used to treat. (See list for members at the end of this task.)

"It is important to understand that while a minor tranquilizer like Librium might re-duce anxiety in a person with a phobia or fear of going places, it may have no effect on the anxiety experienced by a person who suffers from schizophrenia. Each type of drug has its uses for specific problems and specific illnesses. Your physician works with you to discover which type of medication will best reduce the kind of problems that affect you."

Anti-Psychotics or Major Tranquilizers

"Major tranquilizers, also called antipsychotics and neuroleptics, are specifically useful for reducing the symptoms of schizophrenia. These medications come from five separate families of chemicals, but all share the same beneficial or therapeutic effects. Therapeutic effects don't differ from one type of drug to the next; they're all similarly helpful in relieving the symptoms of schizophrenia. However, each drug has special side-effects, and the choice of a drug is often based on its producing the least bothersome side-effects in an individual."

You can discuss some of the major tranquilizers in use today. (See list for members.)

Therapeutic Effects of Major Tranquilizers

The anti-psychotic drugs useful in schizophrenia relieve, reduce, and many times *eliminate* the symptoms of this illness. These drugs are also effective in *preventing* you from experiencing a relapse of your illness. Without major tranquilizers, most schizophrenics will reexperience unpleasant, disruptive symptoms. Return of symptoms occurs in 70 percent of patients with schizophrenia within one year of stopping medication. This can be reduced to a 30 percent relapse rate through continuing maintenance use of medication. In other words, most patients who stay on major tranquilizers will not have a relapse.

"It may be necessary for you to continue using your medication for many years or even your entire lifetime in order to control the symptoms of schizophrenia and to enable you to function well. While most of the unpleasant side-effects of medication are mild and

Common Psychiatric Drugs

Type of Drug	Drug Name	Used To Treat
Anti-Psychotics or Major Tranquilizers	Thorazine Mellaril Stelazine Prolixin	Schizophrenia Mania or "highs" in Bipolar Disorder
Mood Stablizers	Lithium	Bipolar Disorder
Antidepressants	Tofranil, Elavil, Sinequan, Vivactil	Severe Depression
Minor Tranquilizers	Librium, Valium, Equanil, Serax,	Anxiety Disorders
Sedative-Hypnotics/ Sleeping Medication	Seconal, Nembutal, Doriden, Dalmane, Chloral, Hydrate, Quaalude	Insomnia

Major Tranquilizers (Anti-psychotics)

Generic Name	Trade Name	Equivalent Dose	Daily Dose Range
Chlorpromazine	Thorazine	100 mg.	50–2000 mg.
Thioridazine	Mellaril	100 mg.	50–1000 mg.
Perphenazine	Trilafon	8 mg.	8–80 mg.
Trifluoperazine	Stelazine	5 mg.	10–60 mg.
Fluphenazine*	Prolixin	2 mg.	4–80 mg.**
Thiothixene	Navane	2 mg.	4–80 mg.
Haloperidol	Haldol	2 mg.	4–100 mg.
Loxapine	Loxitane	10 mg.	20–250 mg.
Molindone	Moban	10 mg.	10–250 mg.

(*also available as long-acting injection; **long-acting injection — 25–50 mg. every two weeks)

Task 53

temporary, there are some that are very bothersome. It is necessary for you and your psychiatrist to work together to find the right balance between maximum benefits and minimum side-effects of medication. This requires patience in trying different medications and different doses. You and your doctor should be prepared to increase the dose of the medication during times of special stress and when symptoms recur and to reduce the dose when the symptoms are gone in order to provide the least possible amount necessary to maintain functioning and prevent relapse.

"Anti-psychotic medication produces significant improvement in about 75 percent of patients with schizophrenia."

At this point, as the leader you can go over the members' list of "Symptoms Most Likely To Improve" with medication.

"While medication helps almost everyone with schizophrenia, it will probably be just a part of your overall treatment. Medication reduces or eliminates symptoms, but it does not help a person learn new skills, make and keep friends, or know how to get a job. Other forms of rehabilitation and therapy are necessary in combination with medication to produce the best and most lasting results.

"Medication makes it easier for people with schizophrenia to benefit from these other important types of therapy. While taking medication, you will probably be less distracted by symptoms and more able to learn a variety of important new skills."

Side-Effects of Major Tranquilizers

"Almost all of the side-effects to major tranquilizers are temporary and mild. Even the most bothersome side-effects are not harmful to the body and do not last more than the first few weeks or months of treatment. After using the medication for a month or two, most of the annoying side-effects disappear or are greatly diminished."

Talk about the common and uncommon side-effects noted in the members' list.

Minimizing the Problem of Side-Effects

"While most of the side-effects of major tranquilizers are mild and will go away by themselves after a few weeks or months, it is possible to counteract the side-effects with other drugs, by reducing the dose, or by changing medication to another drug without the annoying side-effect. For example, Artane, Cogentin, Akineton, and Amatadine can counteract the symptoms of restlessness, uneasiness, jumpiness, tremor, rigidity of muscles, and involuntary movements of muscles. These drugs are called Anti-Parkinsonian agents because the symptoms they control are similar to the symptoms of people who have Parkinson's Disease. After two to three months of taking a major tranquilizer, most of these side-effects will go away on their own and your doctor can discontinue the Anti-Parkinsonian drugs used to control the side-effects. When the Anti-Parkinsonian drug is withdrawn, the side-effects rarely come back.

"Benadryl (an antihistamine drug) can be given by injection to stop immediately a severe muscle spasm or contraction which is drug-related (stiff neck, eyes rolled up, thick tongue). Emergency rooms and doctors can give this injection which gives almost instantaneous relief.

"Reduction of the medication dose will often reduce or eliminate side-effects.

"Switching to another drug that doesn't have the same side-effects can be another way of coping with problems from side-effects. For instance, Prolixin tends to produce muscle side-effects but Mellaril does not. Switching from Prolixin to Mellaril can solve the problems of muscle rigidity, restlessness, and tremors.

"Likewise, if one drug produces an allergic skin rash, you can be switched to another drug that you are not allergic to."

Maintenance Drug Therapy

"One of the most important causes of relapse in schizophrenia is failure to continue

Symptoms Most Likely To Improve:

- hallucinations, hearing voices, talking to yourself
- delusions and bizarre, unrealistic thoughts
- poor concentration
- disorganized, nonsensical speech
- agitation, pacing, and hyperactivity
- isolating yourself from others and being suspicious
- hostile and aggressive behavior
- emotional displays that don't make sense
  (for example, laughing or crying for no reason)

Common Side-Effects of Major Tranquilizers

drowsiness and tiredness
nasal stuffiness
dry mouth
blurred vision
restlessness, uneasiness,
    jumpiness
contractions and involuntary
    muscle movements

dizziness
(especially
when getting up
too fast from a
chair or bed)
weight gain
tremor or rigidity
of muscles

Uncommon Side-Effects

menstrual irregularities
loss of ejaculation
sensitivity to sunburn
skin darkening
semi-permanent involuntary
    movements of mouth
    and fingers

skin rash
yellow jaundice
nipple discharge
nausea and
    constipation
blood abnormalities

Task 53

taking medication after the symptoms go away. Unfortunately, on the average, 40 percent of patients stop taking their prescribed medication within the first year after leaving the hospital. This produces the 'revolving door' phenomenon, with patients being admitted to and discharged from hospitals repeatedly. There are many reasons for prematurely stopping major tranquilizer drug therapy. By thinking about these factors, you may be able to prevent yourself from making the common mistake of stopping medication before it is advisable."

Relate the following facts to the members.

• "Several patients never fully or even partially understand the nature and seriousness of their illness, nor do they appreciate the need to take anti-psychotic medication indefinitely.

• "Several patients experience uncomfortable and often disabling side-effects, the most disturbing one not easily seen by the doctor or by relatives—uneasiness and feelings of internal jumpiness, feeling slowed down, lifeless, and lacking spontaneity. Other side-effects of drugs include general feelings of discomfort. These side-effects are often overlooked by the physician, but not by the patient, who then abandons medication only to suffer a relapse.

• "Taking medication reminds people that they are sick, which can sometimes make them feel less good about themselves. Sometimes patients will stop taking their medication so that they can ignore the fact that a problem exists.

• "Some patients never understand the connection between stopping drug therapy and relapse because it often takes weeks or even months for the body to use up and metabolize all the medication that had been stored. A person can temporarily feel very well without taking the prescribed drug, since the medication continues to exert its effectivenss and the side-effects are somewhat less. It may take three, four, or even more relapses before a patient puts one and one together and realizes that the relapse occurs weeks or months after stopping the medication.

• "Patients who return to using 'street drugs' like marijuana, LSD, PCP, or amphetamine can suffer relapses since they mistakenly believe that these drugs can help their symptoms. In fact, these drugs can exacerbate the problems of schizophrenia.

• "It is difficult to remember to take medication every day. Unless a person gets into a routine—a special place for the medication and a special time to take it—it is very easy to forget. It is a bother to have to be reminded about the medication, and some patients rebel against family members who try to help by reminding.

• "To help you maintain yourself on any prescribed medication after discharge, remember how important these drugs are for your continued success. Try to make it easy for yourself to remember to take the medication by keeping the bottle in a visible location where you easily reach it. Think about where it would be good to keep your medication once you've left the hospital and are on your own. By planning in this way, you can help yourself become one of the many schizophrenics in the community who are leading satisfying, capable lives."

After discussing the above, ask members to consider the facilities and people they can turn to for future health-care needs and for answering questions. Help the group rehearse assertive ways to ask questions about medications and side-effects. Have members role play raising a concern about medication at a treatment team meeting. Then discuss how to obtain help from others after discharge. Point out that when they go for community mental health appointments, they should frequently discuss medication and its effects and side-effects with their physician or psychiatrist. Mention that it might be advantageous to let family or roommates know why continuing medication is important. Discuss the possibility of asking friends or family to remind members to take their medications, if sometimes they forget.

54   Enjoying My Free Time

Therapeutic Rationale
This activity assists members in developing more satisfying means of using their free time. Group members become aware of one another's interests and hobbies, and learn how to make arrangements for pursuing different recreational activities. Patients are encouraged to work collectively at developing new, shared leisure-time activities. This promotes socialization among members and builds a more effective support network among patients.

Materials
overview sheets
a deck of cards for each group member
simple puzzles
a few local newspapers
local phone book

Procedure
Begin by having members turn to their task overview sheet. Discuss the different things that members enjoy doing during their free time. Ask members to share a special time in their life, including information about where, when, with whom, and why it was special. Suggest the following possibilities if it is difficult for members to recall an event: day at the beach, horse-back riding, holiday party, a beautiful walk, going to a dance, playing Bingo, reading, etc. Have patients also share their favorite routine pastimes.

Next, discuss any supplies needed for particular favorite activities mentioned earlier. Have the group consider inexpensive ways of obtaining these supplies for certain hobbies, for example, checking out Goodwill stores, asking occupational therapist, etc. Solicit ideas about where books, movies, records, sports equipment, games, magazines, etc. can be borrowed for temporary use (hospital recreation department, local libraries, etc.). If members voice an interest in gardening, ask if they'd enjoy rooting some plant cuttings at the next meeting, so that each member could have a plant to nurture.

Have members think about a new game they could learn to play. Distribute decks of cards and teach members how to shuffle the deck. Ask participants to share information about any card games they know. The leader can demonstrate how to play some simple games such as "Go Fish" and "War." Encourage members who enjoy playing cards to set up a date for playing before the next group meeting. Provide simple puzzles for those who dislike playing cards.

Finally, have members review the activities available to them in the community. Use the newspaper and phone book to practice finding special activities (free exhibits, free concerts, museums, movie and television listings) and the locations of area parks, libraries, theatres, churches, zoos, etc. A group field trip to some community event is ideal.

Overview Sheet

GIT Task 54: Enjoying My Free Time

What Do I Like To Do?

What Supplies Do I Need?

What New Game Could I Learn?

What Activities Does the Community Offer?

55 Caring for My Things

Therapeutic Rationale

This task develops skills necessary for more independent functioning, both within an inpatient setting and after discharge to a residence in the community. Learning these skills builds self-efficacy and fosters a sense of mastery. Members are encouraged to become more responsible with their own possessions and to develop greater respect for others' belongings. This improves social functioning and reduces conflicts stemming from inconsiderate handling of other patients' possessions.

Materials

overview sheets
basic sewing kits
buttons
fabric scraps
large models of button, buttonhole (can be made from cardboard), needle, and yarn

Procedure

Have members consult their appropriate task overview sheet and solicit ideas about the items members own that require special care. The group can discuss various clothing types and how some garments are more "maintenance" free (for example, require no ironing) than others. Members might also mention such things as shoes, boots, dentures, glasses, and money.

Have the group consider each type of article, and develop ideas about how to care for each. Discuss laundry practices and local facilities for keeping clothing clean. Members who are more experienced in using the available facilities can demonstrate for less familiar group members. You might mention the value of hanging up clothing when it's not being worn and suggest that members evaluate the adequacy of their closet storage space. If such space is at a premium, patients can be asked to consider paring down their wardrobes to include only those items actually worn on a regular basis. Storing out-of-season garments in boxes liberates scarce storage space.

Ask members whether they regularly polish their shoes in order to keep them looking nice. Members can list any mending needs they have and might be encouraged to bring in their own clothing items that need repair.

Some of the meeting time can be used for teaching participants how to sew on buttons. A large model of a button and button hole, and some yarn can be used for instruction in the basic sewing skills.

Initiate a discussion of how members can keep track of personal items and avoid losing things. Suggest to members that establishing a regular place where glasses, keys, purse, etc. are kept and sticking to that routine can reduce the chance of misplacing items. Have the group talk about specific storage methods used to prevent loss of items. Discuss where the hospital or building lost and found facility is located. Members can talk about what they usually do when they find something that belongs to someone else. Have patients imagine how the person who has lost something feels when the object simply "disappears." By developing empathy in this way, members may become more helpful to one another. The group can also discuss how to care for eyeglasses and what to do if glasses break or become bent.

Conclude the meeting by encouraging a discussion on sharing belongings. Get members to evaluate the advantages and disadvantages of sharing, and to think about practices that can make sharing work more to everyone's advantage — reciprocating sharing with others, being prompt in returning things, not waiting to be asked to return the borrowed item, feeling it's OK not to lend an especially prized possession the owner is afraid of losing.

Overview Sheet

GIT Task 55: Caring for My Things

What Do I Have That Needs Special Care?

How Can I Care for These Things?

How Can I Keep From Losing Things?

How and When To Share Possessions

56   Handling Emergencies

Therapeutic Rationale

This activity prepares group members for different emergency situations they may encounter. Role playing equips members with skills for negotiating awkward situations and for avoiding being victimized. This informational task is especially useful for group members who tend to back away from any new or unfamiliar situation because of an exaggerated fear of an emergency situation. By giving members an opportunity to rehearse constructive ways of handling unusually demanding circumstances, patients become more confident and less hindered by their groundless fears. This can lead to more patient willingness to actively plan for discharge.

Materials

large pieces of paper for recording coping responses
marker

Procedure

You can begin by having members imagine taking a walk in a strange neighborhood while visiting relatives. The group can generate a list of various types of unusual emergencies that could arise in this situation. Remind members that these can be things that rarely happen. Explain that thinking about how to handle such unusual events can leave a person feeling better prepared and relaxed.

Encourage members to include as a possible "emergency" any event that they would find very disturbing or overwhelming. The group may include the following kinds of emergencies:

- Somebody asks you for directions (you are unfamiliar with the area)
- A small child is crying
- You need to use the bathroom
- Someone asks you to get in their car
- Someone wants your money
- There is a car accident
- You get lost

Have members discuss each of the emergencies they have listed, examining the factors to consider before deciding how to respond. Offer suggestions about safe, appropriate ways of dealing with each of the situations. Encourage members to challenge your suggestions if they see a problem, so that the group can work collectively to generate really good solutions to these difficult situations. By doing this, you can reduce the chances of making patients feel that there is one and only one *right* way to handle a given situation. Support efforts at independent problem solving.

You can organize role playing each of the above situations. Encourage members to give one another supportive feedback. These exercises can increase perceived efficacy and willingness to take risks.

Ask members to list any other emergencies that they'd like to know how to handle more effectively. Examples of emergencies that might be discussed include:

- accident: you fall down; cut yourself
- sudden sickness
- bad weather (lightning; glare ice)
- light bulb burns out
- electricity goes off
- telephone does not work
- water pipe starts leaking
- someone else gets hurt or sick
- you are the first to see a fire
- you are out shopping and miss your bus or train

As each of the emergency situations are discussed, you can emphasize the value of staying calm and thinking out actions to take. For each situation, generate ideas about *what you can do* and *where to get help*. Again, role play these situations and give encouraging feedback that highlights the strengths of the responses made by members. During role play, gently offer additional suggestions for improvement. At the end of the final session devoted to this topic, ask members if they feel better equipped to handle an emergency if one were to arise.

57   Choosing Gifts for Others

Therapeutic Rationale

Gift-giving is a way of communicating caring and sustaining relationships. This activity helps patients develop gift selection skills and discover ways of obtaining inexpensive gifts for others. The task also fosters empathy and the ability to take another person's perspective, both of great importance to successful social relationships.

Materials

overview sheets
materials for the simple craft project selected by members (this might be based on an earlier GIT task)

Procedure

After turning to the appropriate task overview sheet, ask how participants feel about giving and receiving gifts. Do any members feel burdened by holiday expectations to exchange gifts with others? Do any feel awkward when they receive a gift and feel that it will be impossible for them to reciprocate in kind? Do any have the urge to do more gift-giving, but feel hopelessly constrained by a tight budget? Let members know that this activity will give them a chance to tackle some of these gift-related difficulties.

Ask members if there is anyone that they would currently like to present with a gift. Several members may find this issue difficult, because many may not feel close enough to another to make them want to exchange gifts. You might suggest the possibility of sharing a gift with a fellow patient or staff member.

Another possibility is to have members think about "adopting" children on a ward of a medical hospital and working to make presents for them. The group can discuss the needs they imagine these children to have, which also provides an outlet for members to express their own lonely, isolated feelings. This is an especially useful direction to pursue in institutions around the holiday seasons, when many members will not be visiting relatives and a large number of the staff will be away on vacation.

Discuss when it is appropriate to exchange gifts, for example, Christmas, Chanukah, birthdays, as tokens of thanks, etc. Have the group consider how getting an unexpected surprise gift makes the recipient feel. Discuss the positive feelings associated with receiving something, but also evaluate the negative feelings which can arise when a person believes he or she is now obligated to return the gesture. Tell members that some people may derive much greater pleasure from a very modest "token" gift than from an expensive purchase that makes them feel encumbered by the need to reciprocate. Discuss ways of presenting a gift that prevent the recipient from feeling unduly obligated.

Have members think about what they would like to receive. Fantasizing can be an enjoyable way of discovering what a person needs to know about someone else in order to select a gift that another would especially enjoy. Discuss the kinds of personal information used in selecting terrific gifts, for example, other person's interests, hobbies, size, favorite color, needs, etc. Have members talk about the best gift they ever received. Inquire about what made it wonderful. Did it meet a special need they had? Did it reflect a lot of caring and planning? Did it make them feel special?

Next, focus on the practical matter of developing inexpensive gift alternatives. If members have access to volunteer organizations that provide a gift fund or gift store-

GIT Task 57: Choosing a Gift for Another

Who Would I Like To Give a Gift?

What Would I Like To Receive?

What Would They Like To Receive?

How Can I Get the Gift?

house, have members share their "insider" information with one another in order to increase use of such resources. Discuss how to make simple gifts, which communicate considerable caring because of the time they take to be planned and created.

Have the group discuss a few craft project ideas and select a simple one to complete. Explain the idea of having a gift on hand just in case a situation arises in which a member would like to present a gift on the spur of the moment. The group can consult a crafts book, or use some of the simple projects described in earlier GIT tasks. Members can contact the occupational therapy department to see what supplies for gift-making are available. At the next meeting, help members assemble supplies for the gift-making task and prepare the gifts.

58 Getting Along With Others

Therapeutic Rationale

This activity extends the GIT social skills developed earlier and provides additional role-playing experiences for developing more assertive ways of handling interpersonal situations. The experience builds an appreciation of the reciprocal nature of relationships, increases empathy, and facilitates relationships among group members. A more effective patient social support system is established. In the past, participation in this task has been associated with significant patient improvement and increased possibilities for successful discharge.

Materials

overview sheets
copies of the "Different Ways People Can Be" sheet (see GIT Task 51)
copies of Role-Plays sheets (if members have good reading skills)

Procedure

Begin by having members consult their task overview sheet, copies of the "Different Ways People Can Be" sheet, and the Role-Plays sheet (if it is appropriate to the reading level of the group membership). Review the adjectives and behaviors on the handout sheet, discussing what the group members like in others. Next, have members consider how they can make their needs known more effectively. You can stress the value of communicating feelings in an assertive fashion. Remind members that it is highly unlikely that others will correctly guess what is wanted. Explain that as a consequence, if patients don't make requests it is improbable that they will ever get what they want. Point out that while making an assertive request certainly does not guarantee that a person will get what he or she ask for, failing to make the request guarantees almost certain failure and frustration.

Help prepare members for the possibility of a rejection of their request. Ask members what they think to themselves after making a request that gets turned down. Consider examples of responses that reflect an acceptance of other people's limitations—"Even though I wanted to have my sister visit, I can understand that she is busy with her job and kids. Possibly I could extend an open invitation so she might come when it's convenient for her." Assist members in developing an outlook about rejections that helps them to take these situations less personally, for example, "The staff member wouldn't lend me money because that's her policy, not because she doesn't like me." Help prepare members for interpersonal failures by encouraging them to view these situations as opportunities to learn how to be even more effective with others—"When a situation turns out badly, I can use it to figure out how to do things better next time." Encourage members to challenge any irrational beliefs and unrealistic expectations they may

Overview Sheet

GIT Task 58: Getting Along With Others

What Do I Like In Others?

How Can I Make My Needs Known?

How Can I Help People Like Me?

12 Ideas for Role-Plays

How am I feeling? What are facial signs, words to use?
- Happy: friendly smiling, be with others.
- Sad: not smiling, sit alone, crying.
- Depressed: quiet, withdrawn, crying.
- Angry: talk loud, fight withothers, unhappy.

Starting a conversation
- Introducing yourself.
- Using small talk (weather, food).
- Listen to what others say.
- End conversation when finished discussing topics.

Praising someone—giving a compliment
- Tell someone what they did for you.
- Tell them why you appreciate it.
- Ask if there is something you could do for them.
- Different things to compliment someone for.
- How to acknowledge a compliment.

Asking for help
- Find out exactly what troubles you.
- Determine if you need help to solve problem.
- Determine who can help—nurse, aide, friend.
- How to communicate the problem to others.

Giving instructions
- What needs to be done and who needs to do it.
- Telling other what you want to be done and why.
- Telling them how to do it and checking their reaction.
- Consider their reactions and accommodate if possible.

Expressing affection
- Decide if you have warm, caring feeling for someone.
- Decide if other person would like to know your feeling.
- Decide how to express your feelings.
- Choose right time to express your feelings.
- Express affection in acceptable manner.

Task 58

Following instructions
- Listen carefully.
- Give your reactions to instructions.
- Repeat or write down instructions.
- Imagine yourself doing instruction, anticipate problem.
- Follow through on instructions.

Assertiveness
- Consider ways you might stand up for yourself.
- Take your stand in direct, reasonable manner.
- Focus on positive rather than negative.

Expressing a complaint
- What is the problem?
- How can the problem be solved?
- Tell others what the problem is and possible solutions.
- Ask for other's response to your complaint.
- Consider the feelings of the other person, come to an agreement.

Expressing anger
- What is making you angry?
- How do you know you are angry?
- Determine how you can best express the angry feelings.
- Express the feelings in an honest manner.

Apologizing
- What do you want to apologize for and why?
- Consider ways to apologize that fit occasion.
- Apologize with honesty and sincerity.
- If appropriate, do something to make up for mistake.

Handling failure
- Decide if you have failed.
- What caused the failure: yourself or circumstances?
- Decide the things that you did right in the situation.
- Determine how you would do things differently if you tried again.
- Decide if you want to try again.

Task 58

have, such as "I should be loved all the time by everyone"; "I should be perfect at everything I try"; "I should never have to feel uncomfortable and anxious."

Ask members how they think others get people to like them. Encourage patients to recognize that "popular" people have learned to

- initiate friendly contacts (others have a chance to be nice in return),
- try to consider the other person's feelings (avoid hurting, attacking, or blaming),
- accept the fact that people have "bad days" (don't take every case of unkindness toward them personally . . . give others a second chance).

Have members discuss each of the twelve topics and issues on the role-playing sheet. Generate a specific illustration of each topic, and have members role play an effective way of handling the situation. Ask members if there are any particular examples of outside group situations they are presently confronting. Invite members to share their own interpersonal "rough spots," and encourage the group to help these members find more effective solutions.

59 Keeping in Touch

Therapeutic Rationale
This activity fosters positive, constructive attitudes toward discharge. Members are given the opportunity to work through their concerns about separation and are reassured about continuing some of the special relationships established in the hospital. Members develop skills useful in maintaining relationships and also come to recognize ways to start social relationships. This encourages the assumption of greater personal responsibility in dealings with others.

Materials
overview sheets
large sheet of paper and marker, or blackboard and chalk
local telephone directories
address book pages
stapler

Procedure
Have members turn to the appropriate task overview sheet and ask them for an update on their discharge planning process. Encourage all members to support specific plans and to show an interest in discussing particular areas members are considering. Foster sharing of detailed information relevant to discharge planning, for example, names of caseworkers, names and addresses of community residential settings, names and addresses of community mental health centers, etc.).

You might mention that even though members have different time frames and not all will be leaving at exactly the same time, all members of the group probably would like to prepare for the time when they will be heading on. Ask if anyone in the group has mixed feelings about leaving the hospital. Help members clarify their ambivalence about leaving by listing the pros and cons of discharge on a piece of paper or a blackboard. Use group discussion of the advantages and disadvantages of discharge to help generate more positive attitudes toward change. If members voice sad, negative feelings about leaving, you might ask them to sit back and imagine a month, then a year, then a decade, and then a few decades going by . . . and imagine still sitting together in this same way in these same chairs. Ask them, "How would it feel if no one in the group ever changed? Would relationships among members start to suffer if no one was moving forward in their lives? What happens when people stop changing? Don't they stop growing, too?"

You can talk about the different views people have of change and new experiences.

Overview Sheet

GIT Task 59: How To Keep in Touch

Different Views of Change

Threat to Security OR Challenge to Grow

Who Do I Want To Keep in Touch With?

What Do I Need To Know About Them?

How To Remember Appointments

How To Use the Telephone to Keep in Touch

Point out that some individuals see change as scary and threatening, and worry that making their life different in some way will be difficult and less satisfying. Tell members that this view of change makes it easy for people to get stuck in a rut, do the same things day after day, and never learn new things. Discuss how this "safe" way to live often results in people spending an awful lot of time worrying that something might happen that could make them change. You can explain that often spending so much time worrying about such things isn't very satisfying. Point out that because in most people's lives events happening around them *do* require them to make changes from time to time, individuals with a very negative view of change find themselves frequently frustrated and angry. They rarely are able to avoid change entirely. Suggest to members that it might be better for them to rethink some of their ideas about change.

Talk about different views of life changes. Tell how some people see new experiences as opportunities for growth and development. Explain how they recognize that a person can thrive when given chances to learn new things, meet new people, and live in new places. Discuss how life with no change could get pretty boring, and that a person who never made any changes in his or her life could also get to be boring.

Get the group to think about change as exciting, which could make it easier for members to deal with circumstances demanding a try at something new. Tell members that instead of becoming angry and pessimistic when new situations arise, they might find it easier to look on the bright side and discover positive aspects of the situation that might otherwise be overlooked.

In leading this discussion, you might ask members if they can remember any time their life changed that elicited a negative response but later was viewed as enjoyable.

Since the biggest "change" in the lives of many group members involved being hospi-talized, and because this change is remembered with sadness and feelings of abandonment and rejection, you should be prepared to help members think about how this *negative* experience also had some *positive* elements. You can discuss how hospitalization may have relieved their temporary fears of being out of control or hurt by others, offered a chance to get some help from other people, an opportunity to be understood and to have some personal difficulties explained, a secure place to live for a while, etc. Reviewing painful thoughts about the initial hospital experience can be a way of reminding members about the things they had to give up—"I missed . . . when I came here," "I couldn't . . . anymore,"—but also helps them to recognize their ability to adjust to challenging circumstances. Remind members that they have worked to develop better skills than they had when they first came to the hospital. Tell them that the acquired skills will allow them to do an even better job of managing the upcoming transitions in their lives.

You might mention that it can be hard to move and leave good friends. Ask members if there are any people with whom they would like to keep in touch after discharge. Members might talk about relatives, friends, staff members, and fellow patients. If a group member cannot identify anyone with whom he or she would like to maintain contact, you might suggest staying in touch with the group.

Have the group consider what kinds of information they need to have about someone they want to maintain contact with. Discuss addresses, zip codes, and phone numbers. Distribute a few address book pages to members and have them staple their own personal phone books. Mention that making regular contacts with people, for example, once or twice a year at holiday time, can keep a friendship going over a considerable distance.

Ask members how they would feel about writing to someone they had not contacted for a few years. Then have members think about how they would feel if a "lost" acquaintance, out of the blue, sent them a postcard. Most members might admit that rather than feeling angry at the person for not having written sooner, they would appreciate the friendly gesture. Tell them to keep this in mind if or when they find themselves in a situation in which they are wondering about whether it's OK to restart communication after a long time.

You might also want to have the group discuss ways of remembering appointments. Review the importance of writing down special appointments on a calendar, and placing the calendar within view. Discuss how to make appointments, taking into consideration other plans for that day and travel time. Give some examples of scheduling situations— "You need to make a half-hour appointment for medication review at the community mental health center, which is near a friend's apartment . . . she gets home from work at five fifteen. How might you combine these trips?" Have the group go through the problem-solving process and evaluate the various alternatives that the different scenarios present.

Finally, have members review telephone usage. Practice looking up phone numbers and writing them in a personal address-phone book. You can conclude this activity by discussing ways that members might wish to keep the group informed about their progress after discharge. Explain that the group will understand if former members are too busy to write long detailed letters, but that an occasional postcard would be immensely appreciated. Have members list the group's address in their personal books. You can go around and write a little reminder next to this address in each member's book, for example, "Don't forget! We want to hear how it's going," "We'll miss you and your good ideas! Send us a postcard!" Remind members of other GIT graduates who have returned to visit or whose postcards have been read and enjoyed at group meetings.

60 Graduation and Aftercare Planning

Therapeutic Rationale (*Graduation*)
Members who have applied themselves to all the GIT tasks deserve some special form of recognition. A group dinner out is an appropriate way of marking this graduation event.

Procedure
If budgetary limitations preclude simply taking available funds for a special dinner, it can be fun to arrange some sort of fundraising activity to earn the group money for graduation. A popcorn, coffee, or sandwich sale can get a group an adequate sum in a short time, if staff members are encouraged to help support the effort.

Therapeutic Rationale (*Aftercare Planning*)
Planning for aftercare increases members' chances for long-term success in the community. It facilitates ongoing use of treatment resources within the community and eases the discharge transition.

Materials
copies of aftercare handouts 1 (see sample of information to include in the patient's handout) and 2.

Procedure
You can help members organize thoughts about discharge by outlining issues they will be discussing with their social worker:

1. potential sources of income
2. living arrangements
3. use of time: scheduling work and recreation
4. education and rehabilitation
5. treatment in the community

Next, provide members with a handout of useful aftercare information tailored to the locality (the social work department may prove to be an invaluable resource in developing this handout). A second handout describing signs of relapse should be distributed to help alert patients to these signs, and to establish a commitment to self-monitoring among patients who are anticipating discharge.

Use the group meeting to discuss the following steps involved in seeking help from agencies:

1. Plan and rehearse what to say before calling. State what is needed clearly and briefly.
2. Prepare for "bureaucratic shuffle," waiting, and being placed on hold. Always get the name of the person spoken to, and write down their phone number and extension at the end of the contact so that they can be contacted directly in the future.
3. If the person called cannot be reached, ask when a return call can be expected, or when the person will be free. If the individual has an answering machine, leave a brief message indicating name, phone number, and when you are likely to be available at that number.
4. If you cannot get the help or information you need, ask to speak with the next person up (supervisor).
5. Learn which branch of government is responsible for an agency. It is necessary to know in order to find them in the telephone book.

Sample Handout 1

Mental Health and Related Services

State—Department of Mental Health, Office of Continuing Care

Staff: social workers, psychiatrists (part-time), psychologists (part-time)

Services: psychotherapy and crisis counseling, medication, living arrangements, income planning, community liasons

County—Community Mental Health Centers

Staff: social workers, psychiatrists, psychologists, nurses, paraprofessionals (sometimes)

Services: psychotherapy and crisis counseling, medication, *access* to partial hospitalization, *access* to inpatient facilities

List of Branch Offices With Phone Numbers

Private Therapists and Counseling Services

Staff: psychiatrists, psychologists, social workers, counselors

Services: psychotherapy, medication (psychiatrists), partial hospitalization, inpatient arrangments

Task 60

Sample Handout 2

Warning Signals of Relapse

- Sleeplessness or other problems at night, such as
    frequent waking during the night
    pacing during the night
    need to drink fluids during the night
- Drinking of alcohol and other drug use
    difficulty in avoiding alcohol use
    begin to drink more than one beer a day
    smoking grass or using other street drugs
- Increased activity (agitation)
    talking inappropriately
    interrupting others
    laughing and crying inappropriately
- Depersonalization
    absence of thought or blanking out
    weakness of body
    feeling of flating away
    feeling depressed and unhappy
- Loss of appetite and interest in eating
- Stopping taking care of yourself and grooming
- Withdrawing from others and becoming suspicious
- Changing how you take medication
- Deciding to secretly stop taking medication
- Thinking too much and noticing thoughts racing

Check this list once a week. If you are having any of these symptoms, call your social worker or contact some other mental health resource person.

References

Alley, S. and Blanton, J., Ph.D. "A Study of Paraprofessionals in Mental Health." *Community Mental Health Journal,* 12(2) (1976): 151–160.

American Psychiatric Association. *Diagnostic and Statistical Manual of Mental Disorders,* 3rd ed., Washington, D.C., 1980.

Beck, J.C., M.D., Kantor, D., Ph.D., and Gelineau, V.A., Ph.D. "Follow-up Study of Chronic Psychotic patients treated by college case-aide volunteers." *American Journal of Psychiatry,* 120 (1963): 269–271.

Bell, M.D. and Ryan, E.R. "Integrating Psychosocial Rehabilitation Into the Hospital Psychiatric Service." *Hospital and Community Psychiatry,* 35(10), (1984): 1017–1023.

Beltz, J.F., Drehmel, V.W., and Sivertsen, A.D. "Volunteer: The Community's Participation in Treatment of Schizophrenic Children in a Day Care Program." *American Journal of Orthopsychiatry,* 37 (1967): 221–222.

Bergman, J.S., Ph.D. "Effectiveness of College Students in an Incentive Community Program for Chronic Hospitalized Patients." *Community Mental Health Journal,* 12(2) (1974): 192–202.

——————, "The Effectiveness of College Students as Therapeutic Agents with Chronic Hospitalized Patients." *American Journal of Orthopsychiatry,* 44(1) (1974): 92–101.

Bergstorm, D.A. "Collaborating With the Natural Helpers for Delivery of Rural Mental Health Services." *Journal of Rural Community Psychology,* 3(2) (1982): 5–26.

Bernheim, K.A. and Lekman, A.F. *Working With Families of the Mentally Ill.* New York: W.W. Norton & Company, 1985.

Bernheim, K.F. and Lewine, R.R.J. *Schizophrenia: Symptoms, Causes, and Treatments.* New York: W.W. Norton & Company, 1979.

Brady, J.P., M.D. "Social Skills Training for Psychiatric Patients, Parts 1,2. Concepts, Methods, and Clinical Results." *The American Journal of Psychiatry,* 141(3) (1984): 333–340.

Brown, M.A. and Munford, A.M. "Life Skills Training for Chronic Schizophrenics." *Journal of Nervous and Mental Disease,* 171(8) (1983): 466–470.

Cancro, R. "Individual Psychotherapy in the Treatment of Chronic Schizophrenic Patients." *American Journal of Psychotherapy,* 37(4) (1983): 493–501.

Carkhuff, R.R. and Truax, C.B. "Lay Mental Health Counseling." *Journal of Clinical Psychology,* 29(3) (1965): 426–431.

Carpenter, W.T. "A Perspective on the Psychotherapy of Schizophrenia Project." *Schizophrenia Bulletin,* 10(4), (1984): 599–602.

Cerniglia, R.P., Christensen, E.W., and Horenstein, D. "Group Decision-Making and Self-Management in the Treatment of Psychiatric Patients." *Journal of Clinical Psychology,* 34(2) (1978): 489–493.

Cohen, B.F., Ridley, D.E., and Cohen, M.R. "Teaching Skills to Severely Psychiatrically Disabled Persons" (1983) Unpublished manuscript.

Crosby, R.L. "Community Care of the Chronically Mentally Ill." *Journal of Psychosocial Nursing,* 25(1) (1987): 33–37, 1987.

Derkman, A. and Whitaker, L. "Humanizing a Psychiatric Ward: Changing From Drugs to Psychotherapy." *Psychotherapy: Theory, Research and Practice,* 16 (1979): 204–214.

Docherty, J.P. "Otempora, Omores: Directions in Research on the Psychotherapeutic Treatment of Schizophrenia." *Schizophrenia Bulletin,* 10(4) (1984): 621–623.

Eckman, T., et al. "Training Skills in the Psychiatrically Disabled: Learning Coping and Competence." *Schizophrenia Bulletin,* 12(4) (1986): 631–647.

Fallon, I.R.H., et al. "Family Management in the Prevention of Exacerbations of Schizophrenia." *The New England Journal of Medicine,* 306(21) (1982): 1437–1440.

Fischer, E.H. "College Students as Companions to Longterm Mental Hospital Patient." *Journal of Consulting and Clinical Psychology,* 35(3) (1970).

Fromme, D.K. and Smallwood, R.E. "Group Modification of Affective Verbalizations in a Psychiatric Population. *British Journal of Clinical Psychology,* 22 (1983): 251–256.

Goldstein, A.P., Sprafkin, R.P., and Gershaw, N.J. *Skill Training for Community Living: Applying Structured Learning Therapy.* New York: Pergamon Press, 1976.

Greenblatt, N. and Kantor, D. "Student Volunteer Movement and the Manpower Shortage." *American Journal of Psychiatry,* 118 (1962): 809–814.

Gross, A.M. and Martin, P. "Increasing Attendance to Recreational Therapy in a Rehabilitation Hospital." *International Journal of Behavioral Geriatrics,* 1 (1982): 27–32.

Gruenberg, E.M. "The Social Breakdown Syndrome and Its Prevention." In S. Arieti (ed.), *American Handbook of Psychiatry,* 2nd Ed. Vol 2. New York: Basic Books, 1974.

Gruver, G.G. "College Students as Therapeutic Agents." *Psychological Bulletin,* 76(3) (1971): 111–127.

Gunderson, J.G. et al. "Effects of Psychotherapy in Schizophrenia: Comparative Outcome of Two Forms of Treatment." *Schizophrenia Bulletin,* 10(4) (1984): 564–598.

Harrow, N. and Westermeyer, J.F. "Predicting Outcome in Schizophrenics and Nonschizophrenics of Both Sexes: The Zigler-Phillips Social Competence Scale." *Journal of Abnormal Psychology,* 95(4) (1986): 406–409.

Hartlage, L.C. "Subprofessional Therapists' Use of Reinforcement Versus Traditional Psychotherapeutic Techniques With Schizophrenics." *Journal of Consulting and Clinical Psychology,* 34(2) (1970): 181–183.

Hersch, P.D., Kulik, J.A. and Scheibe, K.E. "Personal Characteristics of College Volunteers in Mental Hospitals." *Journal of Consulting and Clinical Psychology,* 33(1) (1969): 30–34.

Hesse, K.A. "The Paraprofessional as a Referral Link in the Mental Health Delivery System. *Community Mental Health Journal,* 12(3) (1976): 252–258.

Holzberg, J.D., Knapp, R.H., and Turner, J.L. "Companionship With the Mentally Ill: Effects on the Personalities of College Student Volunteers." *Psychiatry,* 29 (1966): 395–405.

──────────, Whiting, H.S., and Lowy, D.G. "Chronic Patients and a College Companion Program." *Mental Hospitals,* 15 (1964): 152–158.

Hyer, L. and Blazer, D.G. "Depressive Symptoms: Impact and Problems in Long Care Facilities." *International Journal of Behavior Geriatrics,* 1 (1982): 33–44.

Kahn, E.M. (1984). "Group Treatment Interventions for Schizophrenia. *International Journal of Group Psychotherapy,* 34(1) (1984): 149–153.

Kanas, N. and Barr, M.A. "Homogeneous Group Therapy for Acutely Psychotic Schizophrenic Inpatients." *Hospital and Community Psychiatry,* 34 (1983): 257–259.

Kane, C. (1984). "The Outpatient Comes Home." *Journal of Psychosocial Nursing,* 22(11) (1984): 19–25.

Karon, B.P. "The Psychoanalytic Treatment of Schizophrenia." In P. Magaro (Ed) *The Construction of Madness.* New York: Pergamon, 181–212.

──────────, Vanderbos, G.R. "The Consequences of Psychotherapy for Schizophrenic Patients." *Psychotherapy: Theory, Research and Practice,* 9 (1972): 111–119.

Klerman, G.L. "Ideology and Science in the Individual Psychotherapy of Schizophrenia." *Schizophrenia Bulletin,* 10(4) (1984): 608–612.

Levitan, G.W., McNally, R.J., and Reiss, S. "Emotionally Disturbed Mentally Retarded People." *American Psychologist,* 37(4) (1982): 361–367.

Liberman, R.P. et al. *Schizophrenia Bulletin,* 12(4) (1986): 631–647.

Magaro, P.A., Talbott, J.A., and Glick, A. "The Inpatient Care of Chronic Schizophrenia." In A.S. Bellack (Ed.), *Schizophrenia: Treatment, Management and Rehabilitation.* Orlando, FL: Grune & Stratton, 1984.

May, P.R.A. "A Step Forward in Research on Psychotherapy of Schizophrenia." *Schizophrenia Bulletin,* 10(4) (1984): 604–607.

Maxmen, J.S. "An Education Model for Inpatient Group Therapy." *International Journal of Group Therapy,* 28 (1978): 321–338.

Meltzer, S.W. "Group Analytic Approaches to Psychotic Patients in an Institutional Setting." *The American Journal of Psychoanalysis,* 42 (1982): 357–362.

Mitchell, W.E. Amicatherapy: "Theoretical Perspectives and an Example of Practice." *Community Mental Health Journal,* 2 (1966): 307–314.

Moriarty, J. "Combining Activities and Group Psychotherapy in the Treatment of Chronic Schizophrenics." *Hospital and Community Psychiatry,* 27 (1976): 574–576.

Nicoletti, P.D. and Flater, L. "A Community Oriented Program for Training and Using Volunteers." *Community Mental Health Journal,* 11(1) (1975): 58–63.

Nowicki, S. and Strickland, B. "A Locus Control Scale for Children," *Journal of Consulting and Clinical Psychology,* 40(1) (1973): 148–54.

Otteson, J. "Curative Caring: The Use of Buddy Groups With Chronic Schizophrenics." *Journal of Consulting and Clinical Psychology,* 47(3) (1979): 649–651.

Pardes, H. "Health Manpower Policy: A Perspective From the National Institute of Mental Health." *American Psychologist,* (1983): 1355–1359.

Parker, G.V.C. and Parsons, L.B. "Personal Attitudes, Clinical Appraisals, and Verbal Behavior of Trained and Untrained Therapists." *Journal of Consulting and Clinical Psychology,* 32(1) (1968): 64–71.

Parsons, P.J., Ph.D. "Building Better Treatment Plans." *Journal of Psychosocial Nursing,* 24(4) (1986): 9–14.

Poser, E.G. "The Effect of Therapists' Training on Group Therapeutic Outcome." *Journal of Consulting Psychology,* 30(4) (1966): 283–289.

Reiff, R. and Reissman, F. "The Indigenous Nonprofessional: A Strategy of Change in Community Action and Community Mental Health Programs." *Community Mental Health Journal,* monograph No. 1, 1965.

Rotter, J.B., Chance, J.E., and Phare, E.J. *Applications of Social Learning Theory of Personality.* New York: Holt, Rinehart, & Winston, 1972.

Scott, D. and Griffith, M. "The Evaluation of Group Therapy in the Treatment of Schizophrenia." *Small Group Behavior,* 13(3) (1982): 415–422.

Serok, S. "Gestalt Group Therapy With Psychotic Patients." *The Gestalt Journal,* 5 (1983): 45–55.

_____, Zemet, R.M. "An Experiment of Gestalt Group Therapy With Hospitalized Schizophrenics." *Psychotherapy: Theory, Research and Practice,* 30 (1983): 417–424.

Selzer, M.A. "Preparing the Chronic Schizophrenic for Exploratory Psychotherapy: The Role of Hospitalization." *Psychiatry* 46(4) (1983): 303–311.

Shadish, W. "Lessons From the Implementation of Deinstitutionalization." *American Psychologist,* 39(7) (1984): 725–738.

Spencer, P.G., Gillspiel, G.R., and Ekia, E.G. "A Controlled Comparison of the Effects of Social Skills Training and Remedial Drama on the Conversational Skills of Chronic Schizophrenic Inpatients." *British Journal of Psychiatry,* 143 (1983): 165–175.

Stanton, A.H. et al. "Effects of Psychotherapy in Schizophrenia: 1. Design and Implementation of a Controlled Study." *Schizophrenia Bulletin,* 10(4) (1984): 520–551.

Talbott, J.A. *The Chronic Mentally Ill: Treatment, Programs, Systems.* New York: Human Service Press, 1981.

Templing, R., and Chambliss, C. "A Locus of Control Scale for Psychiatric Inpatients." (1980), Unpublished Honors paper, Ursinus College, Collegeville, PA.

Torrey, E.F. *Surviving Schizophrenia: A Family Manual.* New York: Harper & Row, 1983.

Umberger, C.C. et al. *College Students in a Mental Hospital.* New York: Grune & Stratton, 1962.

Vernis, S.F. "Effectiveness of Untrained Volunteers With Chronic Patients." *Journal of Consulting and Clinical Psychology,* 34(2) (1970): 152–155.

Wallace, C.J. "Functional Assessment in Rehabilitation." *Schizophrenia Bulletin,* 12(4) (1986): 604–624.

Walsh, M. *Schizophrenia: Straight talk for Family and Friends.* New York: William Morrow & Company, Inc., 1985.

Yalom, I.D. (1983). *Inpatient Group Psychotherapy.* New York: Basic Books, Inc., 1983.

_____, *The Theory and Practice of Group Psychotherapy* (2nd Ed.). New York: Basic Books, 1975.

Special Offer

$2 discount when ordering New Harbinger Books or cassette tapes using the coupon on this page

You get $2 off the total price when ordering from the list of books below (with a full money back guarantee). Or send for our complete catalogue of books and tapes and get the same $2 discount on orders made from the catalogue.

The Relaxation & Stress Reduction Workbook, $12.50 paperback, $22.50 hardcover

Thoughts & Feelings: The Art of Cognitive Stress Intervention, $11.50 paperback, $21.50 hardcover

Messages: The Communication Book, $10.95 paperback, $19.95 hardcover

The Divorce Book, $10.95 paperback, $19.95 hardcover

The Critical Years: A Guide for Dedicated Parents, $9.95 paperback, $19.95 hardcover

Hypnosis for Change: A Manual of Proven Hypnotic Techniques, $10.95 paperback, $20.95 hardcover

The Better Way to Drink: Moderation & Control of Problem Drinking, $10.95 paperback

The Deadly Diet: Recovering from Anorexia & Bulimia, $10.95 paperback, $19.95 hardcover

Self-Esteem, $10.95 paperback, $19.95 hardcover

Beyond Grief, $10.95 paperback, $19.95 hardcover

Chronic Pain Control Workbook, $12.50 paperback, $19.95 hardcover

Rekindling Desire, $10.95 paperback, $19.95 hardcover

Life Without Fear: Anxiety and Its Cure, $9.95 paperback, $19.95 hardcover

---

__ Please send me a free catalogue of your books and tapes. By using this coupon I will be entitled to a $2 discount on orders made from the catalogue.

__ Please send to me the following book(s). Enclosed is my check.

Price

_____ _____

_____ _____

_____ _____

Name _____   less $2 discount   -$2.00

Address _____ sales tax if Calif. res. _____

_____   shipping/handling   1.25

                                 total   _____

Send to: New Harbinger Publications, Department B, 5674 Shattuck Ave., Oakland, CA 94609